Name:

First Steps

Dear Reader

Becoming a Christian is the start of a new life and there is a lot to learn. First Steps aims to lead you step by step to a fuller understanding of what Christians believe and to help you live your life with God.

Jesus once told a story about two builders. The wise one built his house on the rock, the foolish one built his house on the sand. When the storms came, the house on the rock stood firm, but the other one fell down because it had such poor foundations. Jesus said that if we hear his words and put them into practice, then, like that wise man, we will have a firm foundation for our life which will not shift when the storms come. I hope and pray that First Steps will help you build a solid foundation for your life.

John Robertshaw

● Which Bible?

You will need a Bible to use with First Steps. This course has been prepared using the *New International Version*. This popular version can be obtained at any shop which sells Bibles and quite inexpensive editions are available. You can, however, use other versions. There is a comparison of some versions of the Bible on page 72.

How to use this book

• *One-to-one*

First Steps was designed with one-to-one follow-up of new Christians in mind. Find a Christian friend who will spend time going through the units with you. They will be able to help you understand the Bible passages and apply them to your own situations. Your friend may not be a theological expert but should be able to get further help from their church if you run into difficulty. Meeting with a friend to look at a unit once a week works well.

• *In a group*

First Steps can be used in small groups or home groups. Make sure that there is opportunity to apply the teaching to individual situations.

• *On your own*

If you don't know anyone who can help you with *First Steps,* you may wish to work through it alone. Don't try to do it all at once — do one study at a time and spread the whole course over a few weeks.

• *Suggestions*

First Steps is not just a reading book — *it is a study book to use alongside the Bible*. You might find these suggestions helpful:

- If you are unfamiliar with the Bible, you will find a *Quick Bible Guide* on the inside back cover of this book. If you and a friend have similar Bibles, it may be quicker to use *page numbers* to find verses.
- Read and think about all the Bible passages — the main ones are marked with ✱. Don't just answer the questions — find out what you can for yourself from the passages.
- Take turns to read aloud if you are with others.
- Write answers to the questions in the spaces provided. Try to get the answers from the Bible passages — don't make them up yourself.
- Make a note of any other things which strike you in the passages. Discuss them with your friend or in your group.
- Pause to think, pray, act etc when suggested.
- Don't rush. Take your time. Each unit should take between 30 minutes and an hour.
- When you have finished a unit, look through it to see what you have learned. It may help to go through it again later.

Think!

Unit 1

Becoming a Christian

To become a follower of anyone requires a *decision* — I must *choose* to follow. A Christian is a follower of Jesus and so:

- I cannot be born a Christian.
- I am not a Christian because my parents are.
- I am not a Christian because I live in a 'Christian country'.
- I am not a Christian because I go to church.
- I am not a Christian because I do good things.
- I am not a Christian because I have been baptised or confirmed.
- I am not a Christian because I believe in God.

● So what does it mean to become a Christian?

I become a Christian when I accept what God has done for me and decide to follow Jesus.

Becoming a Christian is:

- Discovering that God really loves me.
- Making a relationship with God so that he can help and guide me in my life.
- Leaving behind fear, guilt, insecurity and anxiety.
- Finding out that whatever happens in this life, I have a firm promise of everlasting life with God.
- Joining a new family — discovering that God is my Father and that I have lots of new brothers and sisters.
- Working for a new boss — making Jesus my Lord and King.
- Receiving peace, joy and power for living.
- Getting a firm foundation for my life.
- Being born again and starting a new life.

Happy Birthday!

● *The problem*

Many people do not know God or believe in him. This is no surprise to anyone who reads the Bible since it explains clearly why people do not know God.

If you do something which offends another person, then your relationship with them is damaged and you need to put things right. In a similar way, our relationship with God is broken because of the wrong things (sins) which we have done against him.

✱ **Isaiah Ch 59: v 1-2** ('iniquities' is another word for sins)

What does sin do? ______________________________

✱ **Romans Ch 3: v 23**

Who has sinned? ______________________________

Checklist – have I sinned?

Here are some of the things described as sins in the Bible. Tick the ones which you have done – ever – in your life!

❑ Hate	❑ Pride	❑ Jealousy, envy	❑ Selfishness
❑ Anger	❑ Stealing	❑ Dishonesty, lies	❑ Spite
❑ Bitterness	❑ Resentment	❑ Ignoring God	❑ Drunkenness

❑ Sexually immoral thoughts ❑ Sexually immoral acts

❑ Occult practices ❑ Taking God's name in vain, swearing

This separation from God means that:

- We are out of touch with God and miss his help and guidance.
- We are slaves of this world and of evil.
- We will die without God and be lost forever.

God

Sin

✱ **Romans Ch 6: v 23**

What are the wages of sin?______________________

What is the free gift of God?____________________

A wage is earned and is what we deserve and reflects the justice of God. A free gift is given even when we don't deserve it and reflects the love and mercy of God.

● *God's solution*

Some people try to remove their own sins, perhaps by being very good or religious. Although this might sound like a good idea, it does not succeed in removing past sins or give power to overcome temptation and sin in the future.

The ***GOOD NEWS*** is that Jesus died to take away our sin and he arose from the dead to give us new power to live the way God wants.

✱ Romans Ch 5: v 8

How did God show his great love for us?

____

✱ 1 Peter Ch 2: v 24

What did Jesus do as he died on the cross (or tree)?

____

✱ 1 Peter Ch 3: v 18

Who was the righteous person? ______________________

Who are the unrighteous people? ______________________

Why did Jesus die? ______________________________

Jesus is the only perfect, sinless person who has ever lived. He is the only person who could die in our place as a *substitute* to take the punishment for our sins.

He was separated from God on our behalf so that our relationship with God can be restored. He suffered as he took our sins away.

✱ Matthew Ch 27: v 32-50

Read the account of the crucifixion of Jesus. What do you make of the cry in verse 46 "My God, my God, why have you forsaken me?"?

____

____

● Our response

Becoming a Christian is responding to what God has done so that it becomes true for you personally. It is like receiving a gift which is offered to you.

How do I respond? — three helpful words

• Repent

This is *saying sorry to God* for the wrong thoughts, words and actions you have done. There may be particular serious sins which you need to mention specifically to God and apologise for.

Repenting also means *renouncing sin* and *turning away from evil.* You can ask God to give you power to live a better life in the future. You may also need to apologise to people you have hurt and put right what you have done wrong (*Acts Ch 3: v 19*).

• Believe

Believing is *having faith in what God has done for you* in sending Jesus to die for your sins. *Thank God* for loving you so much that he sent Jesus to die for you and tell him that you love him and wish to serve him. Thank him for forgiving your sins *(John Ch 3: v 16).*

• Receive

Invite Jesus to come into your life to be your *new boss* (Lord), and your guide. Think of your life as a house and invite him into all the rooms and areas (*John Ch 1: v 12, Revelation Ch 3: v 20).*

If you have not already done so, you could pray to God using the ideas above and become a Christian today!

Action!

● Making it definite

You become a Christian when you repent and believe and take Jesus as your Lord. There are other things you can do to show that you mean business with God:

- *Tell other people* that you are now a Christian.
- *Get baptised* — a sign of your faith in Jesus.
- *Join a church.*
- *Pray and read the Bible* — each day if possible.
- *Ask God to fill you with his Holy Spirit.*
- *Continue with this course!*

For your own benefit, you could sign here with the date.

I have become a Christian ______________________________

Unit 2

A Child of God

Everybody in the world is made by God. He knows every detail of our lives and he loves us. Because God is our creator, he is everybody's Father in this respect — but our sins have separated us from him and we are no longer part of his family. He longs for us to return to him and become his children again. This is what happens when you become a Christian.

✱ John Ch 1: v 6-13

Who is the light of the world? ____________________

(also see John Ch 8: v 12)

What have most of the people in the world done with Jesus?

They did not ____________________ (v 10)

They did not ____________________ (v 11)

What two things must you do to become a child of God (v 12)?

- ____________________
- ____________________

When we become God's children, we are born of ____________ (v 13)

This is sometimes called being 'born again'; it is another way of saying that we have become Christians.

✱ John Ch 3: v 1-7

What can we do when we are born again?

- ____________________ (v 3)
- ____________________ (v 5)

● New life — new start

Being born again is starting a *new life with God*. When a baby is born it needs to grow, learn, get to know its parents and become part of a family. As a 'newborn' Christian, you will need to grow, learn, get to know your heavenly Father and become part of your new family.

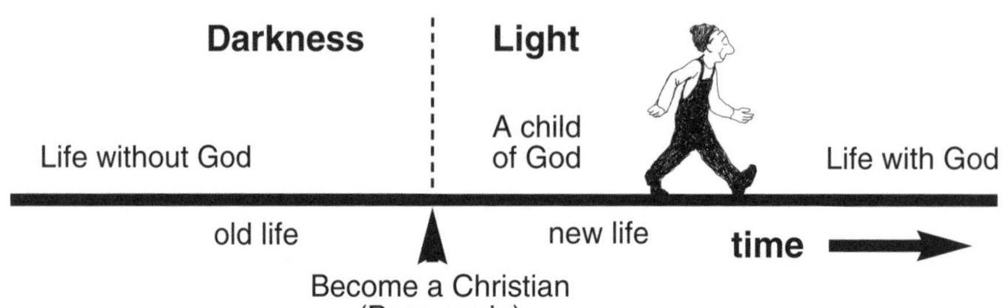

● Part of God's plan

Although you decided to become a Christian, it may surprise you to learn that it was all part of God's plan. Since God can see into the past and the future, he has no surprises! He sees your life from beginning to end — he knows you very well *(Psalm 139: v 13-16)*. What is more, since you have returned to your Father, he can now help you to find his plan and purpose for your life. God can help and guide you with your career, your marriage — every part of your life, as you invite him in.

❋ Proverbs Ch 3: v 5-6

What must you do to allow God to guide you?

● Getting to know your Father

You can find out a lot *about God* by reading the Bible, meeting with other Christians, reading Christian books or listening to CDs, DVDs, online media etc., but you need to cultivate your own *relationship with God.* To do this, you need to talk to him (pray), tell him that you love him and share your life with him — you will soon find that he is very real to you.

❋ John Ch 14: v 23-24

How else can we show our love for God and get to know him?

● A good Father looks after his children

God is interested in every detail of your life and, like any good father, he wants to help you, encourage you, see you do well and correct you if you make mistakes. Now you are a child of God, you can live your life with confidence in the care of your heavenly Father. You will still have problems and difficulties, but you will find that Father can help you through them.

✱ Matthew Ch 6: v 25-34 What should we not worry about?

- ____________________ • ____________________
- ____________________ • ____________________

What should we seek instead (v 33)?

____

Worry comes from fear and insecurity. Millions of people today suffer from anxiety, fear, depression and guilt — *Jesus came to enable us to live in peace and security instead!*

Things people worry about (Tick the ones which apply to you)

❑ Uncertain future ❑ Losing my job ❑ War
❑ Fear of illness ❑ Meeting people ❑ Debts, money
❑ Losing friends ❑ Being alone ❑ Work
❑ Clothes ❑ My appearance ❑ Death
❑ Relationships with people ❑ What people think of me
❑ Political situations ❑ Getting stuck in a rut
❑ Failure in job, marrriage, college course etc
❑ Being found out for things done in the past
❑ Others: ____________________________

Right now — talk to God, tell him about your worries and problems and hand them over to him. You can leave each of these heavy burdens with God. Read *Matthew Ch 11: v 28-30.*

✱ Philippians Ch 4: v 6-7

What does God promise instead of anxiety?

____

● *Your Father is generous*

✱ Matthew Ch 7: v 7-11

Ask and it will be __________________________

Seek and you will __________________________

Knock and the door will ________________________

What kind of gifts does God give to his children?

____

Don't be afraid to ask God for things. He can work through your financial problems with you, he can heal your body, he can help you with relationships — he can move mountains if you have faith!

✱ Matthew Ch 17: v 20

How much faith do we need to move a mountain?

____

● *Heavenly Daddy*

✱ Mark Ch 14: v 35-36

Jesus knew that he would soon be crucified. How did he refer to his Father when he was in distress? ____________

This is the intimate word for 'daddy' in the local language which Jesus spoke (Aramaic).

✱ Galatians Ch 4: v 6

Who helps us to relate to our heavenly Daddy? ______________

● *Growing up*

As you move forward as a Christian, you will learn to trust God more and know him better. As you read the Bible, you will discover the many promises which God has for you and the joy of living each day as a child of God with the support of your heavenly Father.

Unit 3

I Forgive You

● What does 'forgive' mean?

Forgiveness is needed when one person has wronged another and the relationship between the two has been damaged. In order that forgiveness may operate, there must be love and a desire for reconciliation on both sides. Forgiveness and apology go hand in hand.

The person who has done wrong

"I love you. I apologise. I repent. I admit that I have done wrong and am sorry I have hurt you. I wish to put things right."

The person who has been wronged

"I love you. I forgive you. I accept your apology. I wish to forget the wrongs and cast away the hurts that you have caused."

I repent  ***Reconciliation***  ***I forgive***

Repenting means apologising and being determined not to do the same thing again. Often in human situations, both parties need to forgive and repent because there is wrong on both sides.

● God wants to forgive us

✻ Psalm 103: v 8-14

Does God treat us as we deserve? ______________________________

How great is the love of God towards those who fear him?

____

How far does he remove our transgressions (sins) from us?

____

• *Fear the Lord?*

This does not mean that we should be afraid or scared of God. It does mean that we should respect him, honour him and be reverent to him; he is the holy, awesome creator of the whole universe and will be our judge.

ISAIAH

✱ Isaiah Ch 43: v 25

What does God do with our transgressions (sins) when he forgives us?

____

Does God remember our sins?______________________________

When God forgives us, he forgets our sins and does not hold them against us in the future. They are

Forgiven! Forgotten! Gone!

✱ Isaiah Ch 53: v 5-7

This prophecy about Jesus was written by the prophet Isaiah about 700 years before Jesus lived!

What did God do so that we can be forgiven?

____

Because God is holy and just, he cannot merely 'let us off' when he forgives our sins. Jesus died on the cross in our place to take the punishment for our sins.

● Receiving God's forgiveness

✱ 1 John Ch 1: v 9

(This is not John's gospel, but a letter written by John — you will find it near the end of the Bible.)

What must we do to receive God's forgiveness?

____

What else will God do for us?

____

● What if I sin again after God has forgiven me?

Very simply, you need to confess and repent again — but repentance does mean turning away from sin and having the desire and determination to overcome it by the power of God in you!

Salvation

As well as forgiving our past sins, God offers power to overcome sins day by day. When we become Christians, we are saved. Being saved is called salvation.

- ***We have been saved from the penalty of sin***
  Our sins have been forgiven and we need no longer fear the judgment of God.
- ***We are being saved from the power of sin***
  God gives us strength to live wholesome lives.
- ***We will be saved from the presence of sin***
  We have the promise of eternal life — there will be no sin when we are with God for ever after this life.

● As we forgive those who sin against us

Unforgiveness and bitterness are the source of many of our problems. They produce arguments, hate, violence, wars, disintegration of family life, political unrest and breakdown in communication. Sometimes our resentments appear to be justified because we have been badly wronged, or we find it impossible to understand the other person's attitude. Jesus taught a new way of approaching these situations — *we are to treat people as God treats us.*

✱ Luke Ch 6: v 27-36

What should we do for our enemies?

- ________________________ (v 27)
- ________________________ (v 27)
- ________________________ (v 28)
- ________________________ (v 28)
- ________________________ (v 29)
- ________________________ (v 30)

What is our reward? ________________________________(v 35)

In what ways should we be like our Father?

____(v 35-36)

Think!

Review your life and consider if there are people whom you find it hard to forgive, whom you resent, or who have wronged you … they could be:

- parents
- children
- relatives
- husband
- wife
- ex-boyfriend
- ex-girlfriend
- previous spouse
- employer or employee
- landlord or tenant
- schoolteachers
- doctors
- those who have abused you
- friends who have let you down
- people who have influenced your life in a harmful way

Now - Pray for these people and begin to love them knowing that God loves them and cares for them. Extend your forgiveness to them — if you find this difficult, ask God to help you and melt your hard heart. Your forgiveness needs to be like your Father's …

Forgiven! Forgotten! Gone!

✱ Luke Ch 23: v 34

Look at the example of Jesus. What were they doing to him when he prayed for their forgiveness?

____

✱ Matthew Ch 18: v 21-22

What did Jesus mean by 77 times? How often should we forgive?____________________

● A parable about forgiveness

Jesus told parables (stories) to illustrate his teaching. Reading this parable, you can consider what the characters (King, servants) and debts represent. You cannot always draw teaching from the fine details of parables — look for the main point being made.

✱ Matthew Ch 18: v 23-35

What does the large debt represent? ____________________

What does the small debt represent? ____________________

How can we show our gratitude for God's forgiveness?

____

The Bible

Unit 4

• *A big book!*

The Bible is a big book but do not be discouraged by that. You will be surprised how quickly you get to know where things are. It is rather like going to a new town — you soon find out where the main roads are but as time goes by you learn more about the little streets and individual buildings … and you find your own favourite places.

• *A library*

The Bible is actually a library of books written by many different authors over a long time, but because the same Holy Spirit inspired these people, there are many common themes running through the whole of it.

• *God's wisdom*

The Christian faith is not based on human ideas or wisdom but on God revealing himself to mankind. This means that *we cannot make up what we believe* — we must listen to what God says. The Bible is a record of what God has said and done and is our final authority in matters of faith. Jesus and the early Christians frequently referred to the *Scriptures* by which they meant the Old Testament writings.

● The Bible is inspired by God (God-breathed)

✱ 2 Timothy Ch 3: v 14-17

The apostle Paul is writing to a younger man, Timothy. What can reading the Bible do for you?

____(v 15)

All scripture is ______________________________(v 16)

What is the Bible useful for (v 16)?

• ____________________ • ____________________

• ____________________ • ____________________

Reading the Bible will equip you for serving God, teach you the will of God and keep you in the truth and out of error.

● *Use the Bible to check Christian teaching*

❋ Acts Ch 17: v 1-3

Paul was preaching to Jews in Thessalonica. Later, he wrote the two *letters to the Thessalonians* to those who became Christians in this place. Notice how Paul uses the scriptures.

What did Paul explain and prove from the Old Testament scriptures about *the Christ* (the Messiah expected by the Jews)?

The Christ would ______________________________

The Christ would ______________________________

Who did Paul say is the Christ? ______________________

❋ Acts Ch 17: v 10-12

Paul moved to Beroea and preached to the Jews there. These people checked the teaching of Paul carefully and they believed.

How often did they examine the scriptures? ________________

● *Jesus is the key to understanding the Bible*

The Bible reveals the plan of God for the world and mankind. Jesus is central to that plan and he is the key to understanding the scriptures.

❋ John Ch 5: v 39-40

The Bible can be lifeless without the key.

How can we have life? ______________________________

❋ John Ch 5: v 45-47

Who wrote about Christ 1300 years before Christ? ______________

❋ Luke Ch 24: v 44-46

Which parts of the Old Testament speak about Jesus?

- ______________
- ______________
- ______________

These were the three main divisions of the scriptures and Jesus meant the whole of the *Old Testament*. God gave the early Christians a clear understanding of his purposes and enabled people to write more inspired scriptures which became our *New Testament*.

✱ 2 Peter Ch 3: v 1-2, 15-16

In one breath, Peter the apostle talks about the words of the prophets (Old Testament) and the teaching of Jesus as delivered by the apostles (New Testament). He also includes the letters of Paul with the other scriptures.

The Word of God

The expression the **Word of God** is used in a number of ways in the Bible.

- **It is the activity and communication of God.** God created the universe by his Word (Hebrews Ch 11: v 3).
- **The Old Testament laws and prophecies** are the Word of God.
- **The teachings of Jesus and the good news (gospel) of salvation** are the Word of God.
- **Jesus himself** was the most vivid revelation of God to mankind and he is called **the Word who became flesh** (John Ch 1: v 1-3, 14).

Receive the Word of God

The Word of God can come to you in many ways — through your prayers, your conscience, through a conversation, through preaching, through spiritual gifts and of course through reading the Bible. As you read the Bible, expect to receive the Word of God.

● *The Word of God is like a sword*

✱ Hebrews Ch 4: v 12-13

The Word of God is ____________________ and ____________________

The Bible tells us much about the character of God and you will get to know him better as you read it. The Bible also gives clear guidelines as to how we should live and you will find that, like a sword, it divides between good and evil and exposes our actions, thoughts, attitudes and motives.

● *The Word of God is like a mirror*

✱ James Ch 1: v 22-25

Like a true mirror, the Bible gives us a realistic picture of what we are like — and it is not a pretty sight! We must be prepared to submit ourselves to what we read and allow ourselves to be changed by the power of God.

We must not be just hearers of the word, but ____________________

Determine to have a submissive attitude to the Bible. Ask God to help you to understand it as you read it. Tell God that you want to obey his Word and ask for his power to enable you to do it.

● *The Bible encourages, comforts and guides*

✱ Psalm 119

This is a song of praise to God for his commandments, his Word, and his law. It is the longest Psalm!

Pick out the following verses:

- **v 9** How can you keep your way pure?

____

- **v 11** How can you avoid sinning?

____

There is great benefit in learning parts of the Bible so that the Word is in you and ready for times of testing. When Jesus was tempted, he defended himself by quoting scripture which he had hidden in his heart (*Matthew Ch 4: v 1-11*). The Word of God is the *Sword of the Spirit,* part of our armour (*Ephesians Ch 6: v 17*)!

- **v 18** You could say this prayer before you read the Bible. Enjoy the *wonderful things.*

- **v 50** How can we be comforted when we are in trouble?

____

The Bible is packed with the *promises of God*. Find the promises and believe them — God is faithful and true to his Word.

- **v 105** We all need help and guidance in our lives. The Word of God will help you to find your way through the difficult decisions of life.

Get into the habit of reading the Bible regularly - every day if possible. It is, after all, your maker's handbook! You will find more information about the Bible on pages 65-72 of this book.

Water Baptism

Unit 5

In the early days of the church, it was normal for a person to be baptised shortly after he or she became a Christian. It was a definite outward act showing that a person had repented and come to faith in Jesus.

● Jesus was baptised

✱ Mark Ch 1: v 1-11

John the Baptist came to prepare the way for Jesus. Jesus began his ministry after his baptism in the River Jordan. He then preached and healed for two or three years before he was crucified.

The other people who were baptised *confessed their sins* and *repented.* How do we know that Jesus did not need to confess any sins (v 11)?

____

How did the Holy Spirit appear? ______________________________

● Did Jesus baptise people?

✱ John Ch 3: v 22-23, Ch 4: v 1-3

Did Jesus baptise people? ______________________________

Who baptised Jesus' followers? ______________________________

● A command from Jesus

✱ Matthew Ch 28: v 19-20

Before Jesus returned to his Father, he instructed his followers to do *three* things; what were they? • ______________________________

• ______________________ • ______________________

● *The command carried out*

In the book of *Acts* there are many accounts of people being baptised — here are a few:

✱ Acts Ch 2: v 37-41 — Many people

What did Peter say the people had to do to have their sins forgiven?

• ______________________ • ______________________

How many people believed and were baptised? ______________

✱ Acts Ch 8: v 26-40 — An individual

This is an amazing story of God's guidance and timing as Philip joined the eunuch just as he was reading from Isaiah Ch 53. How soon after hearing the good news and believing was the eunuch baptised?

____

✱ Acts Ch 16: v 29-34 — A family

What must you do to be saved?

____

Βαπτιζω *(Baptizo)*

The word *baptism* is from a Greek word meaning to *dip, submerge* or *cleanse by washing.* The word was used for dyeing cloth and involved *immersion.* Christian baptism was by total immersion for those who believed and there was no long period of training before baptism.

● *The meaning of baptism*

✱ Acts Ch 22: v 16

The simplest meaning of baptism is the washing away of our sins — having a big bath! *What are you waiting for?*

✱ Romans Ch 6: v 1-12

Whom are we baptised into? ______________________(v 3)

We are not baptised into a particular church, an organisation, or a denomination. It is an outward act declaring that I have become a Christian and am now one of God's people.

What are we baptised into? ______________________(v 3)

Baptism is a sign that we have been united in the death of Christ.

Which part of us has been crucified? ______________________(v 6)

Why does it need to die?______________________________(v 7)

So baptism is a symbol that your old life is dead. When you are baptised, you can leave the old bad things of the past in the water and rise up into new life.

Action!

Write down two things from your old self which have died since you became a Christian.

____

____

Write down one thing in your life which still needs to die!

____

(The sooner it dies the better!)

When your old self tries to get out of the grave, remind him that he is dead, he went to the cross with Jesus. You are now living a new life in the power of the resurrection of Jesus. You can remind your old self about his funeral service at your baptism!

Count yourself

Dead to________________(v 11)

The old self

Count yourself

Alive to________________(v 11)

New life

As Christ was raised from the dead, so we may

____(v 4)

Our new life starts when we repent and believe in Jesus. Baptism is an outward sign of the work that God has already done in our lives.

Baptism is a symbol

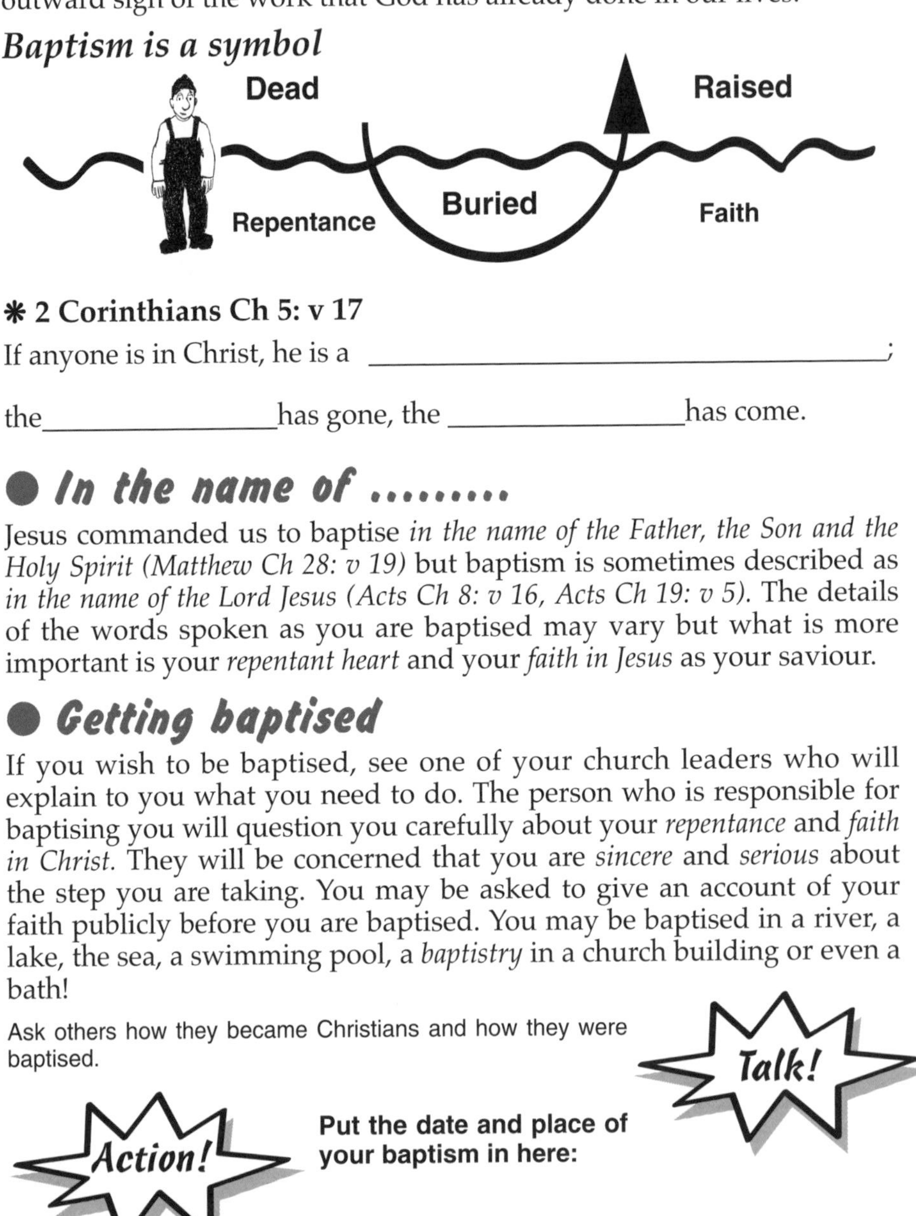

✱ 2 Corinthians Ch 5: v 17

If anyone is in Christ, he is a ________________________;

the_______________has gone, the _______________has come.

● *In the name of ....*

Jesus commanded us to baptise *in the name of the Father, the Son and the Holy Spirit (Matthew Ch 28: v 19)* but baptism is sometimes described as *in the name of the Lord Jesus (Acts Ch 8: v 16, Acts Ch 19: v 5).* The details of the words spoken as you are baptised may vary but what is more important is your *repentant heart* and your *faith in Jesus* as your saviour.

● *Getting baptised*

If you wish to be baptised, see one of your church leaders who will explain to you what you need to do. The person who is responsible for baptising you will question you carefully about your *repentance* and *faith in Christ.* They will be concerned that you are *sincere* and *serious* about the step you are taking. You may be asked to give an account of your faith publicly before you are baptised. You may be baptised in a river, a lake, the sea, a swimming pool, a *baptistry* in a church building or even a bath!

Ask others how they became Christians and how they were baptised.

Talk!

Action!

Put the date and place of your baptism in here:

____

P.S. Churches baptise in different ways. Talk with your church leader to see how baptisms are done in your church.

Unit 6

Bread and Wine

✱ Acts Ch 2: v 42-47

Here we have a window into the vibrant, exciting life of the church in the early days. These few verses are packed with the activities of the Christians in Jerusalem — can you find 10 different activities?

- ______________________________(v 42)
- ______________________________(v 42)
- ______________________________(v 42)
- ______________________________(v 42)
- ______________________________(v 43)
- ______________________________ (v 44-45)
- ______________________________(v 46)
- ______________________________(v 46)
- ______________________________(v 47)
- ______________________________(v 47)

How many of these things are you seeing happen in the church today?

Where did they 'break bread'?

______________________________(v 46)

From the very beginning, Christians have remembered the crucifixion of Jesus by sharing bread and wine together. It is called by various names — *communion, breaking of bread,* the *Lord's Supper* etc.

● Looking back – remembering

❋ Luke Ch 22: v 14-20

This was the last meal that Jesus had with his apostles before he died. Later that evening he was arrested and tried before being crucified on the following day.

The meal was the **Passover**

A detour into history

The place – Egypt

The date – c. 1280 BC

The situation –

You may remember the story. The Israelites were slaves in Egypt and Pharaoh was unwilling for them to leave. God had sent a number of plagues on the Egyptians and the final one was the death of the first-born.

❋ Exodus Ch 12: v 21-28

What kind of animal was sacrificed? ______________________

Where was the blood put? ______________________

Why was it called the 'passover'? ______________________

____

Back to Luke Ch 22 – AD 30

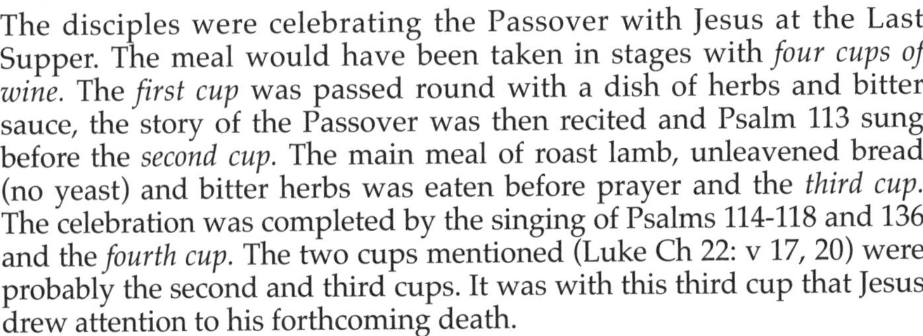

The disciples were celebrating the Passover with Jesus at the Last Supper. The meal would have been taken in stages with *four cups of wine*. The *first cup* was passed round with a dish of herbs and bitter sauce, the story of the Passover was then recited and Psalm 113 sung before the *second cup*. The main meal of roast lamb, unleavened bread (no yeast) and bitter herbs was eaten before prayer and the *third cup*. The celebration was completed by the singing of Psalms 114-118 and 136 and the *fourth cup*. The two cups mentioned (Luke Ch 22: v 17, 20) were probably the second and third cups. It was with this third cup that Jesus drew attention to his forthcoming death.

What did Jesus say the *bread* represents (Luke Ch 22 v 19)?

____

When you take the bread, you can *remember* the suffering of Jesus. He was abused, spat upon, whipped, mocked, dressed in a purple robe, crowned with thorns, deserted by those who had followed him, made to struggle under the weight of the cross and crucified.

What does the *wine* represent? ____________________

____(v 20)

A *covenant* was a contract or promise made between people and in ancient times it was often sealed by shedding the blood of an animal and eating a meal together. Jesus was saying that because he was going to die for the sins of mankind, a new covenant was being made between God and man. Jesus died to reconcile us to God.

✱ 1 Corinthians Ch 5: v 7

Who is our Passover Lamb? ____________________

John the Baptist said of Jesus, "The Lamb of God who takes away the sins of the world."

Because Jesus has died, God will *pass over* our sins and we will escape on the day of judgment.

As you take the wine, *remember* that Jesus died to save you.

Healing

✱ Matthew Ch 8: v 14-17

Jesus died to take away our sins — but what else did he bear?

____

✱ Isaiah Ch 53: v 4-6

What are we healed by (v 5)?

____

✱ 1 Peter Ch 2: v 24

Jesus provides forgiveness and healing by his death on the cross (called a tree here). As you read about the life of Jesus, you will find that healing was a very important part of his work — he came to make us whole in every way. If you are ill or have some physical ailment, don't be afraid to ask God for healing — he can make you better! Many have been healed as they have read the verses above.

● Looking to the present – sharing

✱ 1 Corinthians Ch 10: v 16-17

The cup is ______________________________

The bread is ______________________________

This act is an expression of our *union with Christ.* We belong to him and he is in us.

Communion – the body of Christ

The church is often called the body of Christ. It is through this body that he operates here on earth. As a Christian, you are part of the body of Christ.

The act of breaking bread is also an expression of our relationship to each other. We belong to one body as the fragments of the loaf belong together.

Christ

✱ 1 Corinthians Ch 11: v 27-34

Whom should we examine before breaking bread? ____________________

We should make sure that our relationship with God and other people is good. We should *repent* and *forgive.*

● Looking forward – expecting

✱ 1 Corinthians Ch 11: v 26

We should remember the death of Christ by bread and wine until when?

____

✱ Matthew Ch 26: v 26-29

Where will Jesus have wine again? ______________________________

Who will be with him? ______________________________

✱ Revelation Ch 19: v 6-9

This is a description of the heavenly banquet. What is it called?

____

As we break bread, we look forward to our everlasting fellowship with Jesus — the Lamb who was slain but is now seated on the throne.

Who is the bride of the Lamb? ______________________________

Jesus is Alive

As Christians, our faith is in a *God who really exists* and we are saved because of *events which really happened* in history. We are concerned with **facts**. The most important events are the death and resurrection of Jesus.

● Fact 1 – Jesus died

✱ John Ch 19: v 28-37

To speed up death by crucifixion, the legs of the victim were broken making it more difficult to breathe.

Did they need to break the legs of Jesus? ____________________

Why? ____

What was done to make sure that Jesus was dead?

____

● Fact 2 – Jesus was buried

✱ John Ch 19: v 38-42

What was done with the body of Jesus after it was taken down from the cross?

____(v 40)

Where was the body put? ______________________________

● *Fact 3 – Jesus was raised from the dead*

✱ John Ch 20: v 1-9

Who was the first at the tomb on Sunday morning?

____

What did she see? ______________________________

What did Peter and John see inside the tomb?

____

Jesus had risen from the dead

...there is no other adequate explanation!

Some inadequate theories

Many people have tried to disprove the resurrection — here are some attempts:

- ***Jesus did not really die but revived in the tomb***

— but a man with the injuries which Jesus suffered could not have unwrapped himself, rolled a stone away from the tomb, overcome a Roman guard (see Matthew) and given a convincing show of being raised from the dead!

- ***The disciples stole the body***

— but all the evidence is that the disciples were shocked and fearful after the crucifixion. Remember too that these disciples later suffered persecution and gave their lives for their faith in the risen Jesus. Surely they were not liars!

- ***The authorities stole the body***

— but why didn't they produce it again when the disciples started preaching about the resurrection!

✱ Luke Ch 24: v 36-43

In what *three* ways did Jesus prove that his body had really risen from the dead?

- ____
- ____
- ____

• *Jesus kept appearing to his disciples for several weeks*

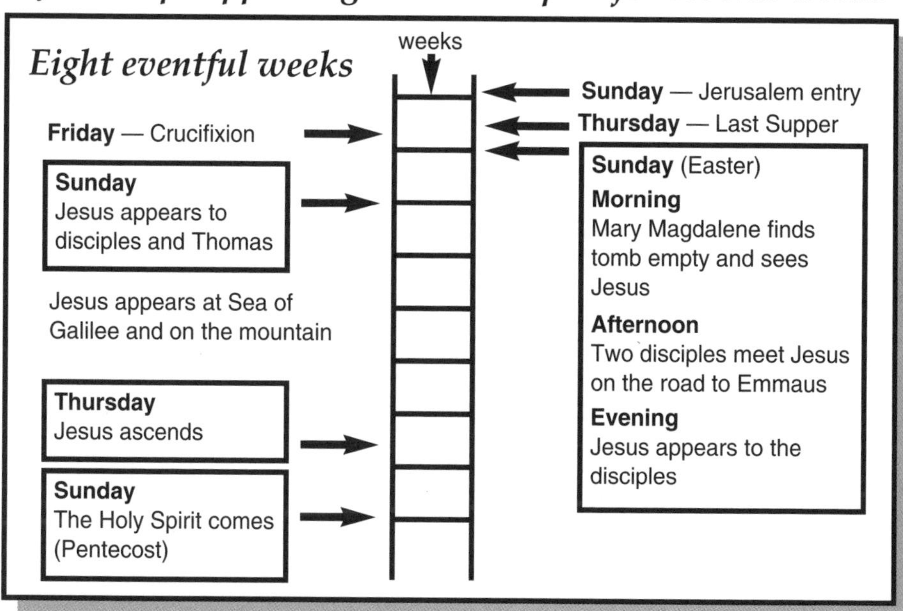

✻ 1 Corinthians Ch 15: v 3-8

Paul wrote this letter about 25 years later. Notice which things he thought were most important — Jesus *died,* was *buried* and was *raised.*

Which three individuals are mentioned as having seen Jesus after his resurrection?

• ________________ • ________________ • ________________

How many people saw Jesus risen on one occasion? ________________

✻ 1 Corinthians Ch 15: v 12-20

The fact of the resurrection is crucial.

If Christ was not raised then ________________________________

and ____(v 17)

Why is the raising of Christ a *first fruit?*

____

✻ Romans Ch 10: v 9 How are we saved?

• ____

• ____

Facts – faith – feelings

You may not always *feel* very close to God. It may be that there is sin in your life which is causing the problem — in which case you must repent. But *feelings* are not always very reliable and as human beings we tend to go up and down with the events of life.

Our faith is based on *fact* not feelings. God does not disappear or forsake us because we do not feel too good!

• *Consider the facts*

- Jesus really did come to earth and die for my sin.
- Jesus really did rise again and will return.
- I have become a Christian — I have repented and have been forgiven.
- God loves me and cares for me — I am his child and he is my Father.
- God has a plan and purpose for my life.
- I can look back and see how God has worked in my life since I believed.
- Jesus has promised his power and his presence whatever the circumstances and however I feel — Jesus is alive!

(Reading the Bible will help you consider the facts.)

• *Exercise faith*

Put your trust in God based on the facts — thank him for his goodness — praise him in all circumstances.

Action!

• *Rule your feelings*

Walk in the power of God exercising faith and you will increasingly find that you are not ruled by your feelings but that you will rule them with God's strength!

❋ Romans Ch 8: v 34

Where is Christ now? ____________________

What is he doing? ____________________

❋ Galatians Ch 2: v 20

Where else does he live? ____________________

❋ Matthew Ch 28: v 20

How long will he stay? ____________________

Unit 8

• Who is he?

Throughout the Bible, we read of *God working in the world through his Spirit.* The Holy Spirit is sometimes called the *Spirit of the Lord,* the *Spirit of God,* the *Spirit of Christ* and often just *the Spirit.*

He is a *person,* not just an influence and it is through the Spirit that God gives *power* and *life.*

- He creates and sustains life.
- He inspires the Bible and helps us to understand it.
- He gives men power to work for God and to speak the Word of God.
- He convinces people of their sin.
- We are born again of the Spirit.
- He gives supernatural power and spiritual gifts to men — he is responsible for the miraculous.
- He helps us to pray.
- He helps us to praise God and glorify Jesus.
- He guides us.
- He helps us to live for God.

The Holy Spirit was gently working in the background before you became a Christian, helping you to understand the gospel and to respond. Now you are a Christian, he can move into the foreground of your life and give you *power for living.*

✱ John Ch 15: v 26
Who sends the Holy Spirit?

____

Where does he come from?

____

● A promise

At the last supper, Jesus explained a lot of things to his disciples (*John Ch 13 - Ch 16*). He said that he would send the Holy Spirit to help them when he had gone.

What did Jesus promise that the Holy Spirit would do?

✱ John Ch 14: v 16-17 ______________________________

✱ John Ch 14: v 26 ______________________________

✱ John Ch 15: v 26 ______________________________

✱ John Ch 16: v 7-8 ______________________________

✱ John Ch 16: v 13 ______________________________

✱ John Ch 16: v 13 ______________________________(prophecy)

✱ John Ch 16: v 14 ______________________________

● Baptised with the Holy Spirit

✱ Acts Ch 1: v 3-9

Before Jesus ascended, he promised his disciples that in a few days' time they would be *baptised with the Holy Spirit* (v 5). This means *immersed* in the Holy Spirit — they were going to receive new *power* (v 8).

What was this power for?

____

Every Christian *has the Holy Spirit* and has been *born of the Spirit* (born again). We need to be *baptised with the Holy Spirit.* Being baptised with the Holy Spirit is an *entry into the power of God.* This is only a beginning and we need to be continually *filled with the Spirit* in order to live effective and powerful lives for God.

✱ Acts Ch 2: v 1-21

What were the outward signs of the coming of the Holy Spirit?

____(v 2-3)

What did the disciples do when they were filled with the Holy Spirit?

____

What were they saying? ______________________________(v 11)

What else can we expect when people are filled with the Holy Spirit?

• ______________ • ______________ • ______________(v 17)

What was the result of Peter's preaching after he had been baptised with the Holy Spirit (v 41)?

____

... They had received power!

Other examples

There are other people mentioned in Acts who were baptised with the Holy Spirit. Look and see what happened to them and tick or cross the boxes.

Were hands laid on them?

Did they speak in tongues?

Acts	People	hands	tongues
2: v 1-4	Apostles and others	✗	✓
8: v 14-19	Samaritans		
9: v 17-18	Paul (see 1 Cor 14:18)		
10: v 44-48	Cornelius's family		
19: v 1-7	Ephesians		

Tongues

This gift may seem rather weird and pointless. You can read more about it in *1 Corinthians Ch 14.* It is a sign of the coming of the Holy Spirit, it can be a great help in personal prayer, it can be spoken out in a meeting and someone may interpret (another gift) and you might sometimes hear people singing in tongues! Why God chose this gift is not stated but it may be to do with the fact that the tongue is a very powerful part of our body which needs controlling — see *James Ch 3: v 1-12.*

● Your turn!

Action!

Have you been baptised with the Holy Spirit?

✱ John Ch 7: v 37-39

If you are thirsty, then you must

______________ and ______________

Ask God to fill you with the Holy Spirit and start to praise him. Ask those who are Spirit-filled to lay their hands on you. Expect to receive a new language (tongue) with which you can glorify God. Move into a new dimension of the power of God and spiritual gifts. Allow the streams of living water to flow out from you.

✱ 1 Corinthians Ch 12: v 4-11

Speaking in tongues is one of the **gifts of the Spirit**. Find *nine* spiritual gifts in this passage.

● Walking by the Spirit - fruit of the Spirit

❋ Galatians Ch 5: v 16-25

How should we live? ______________________________(v 16)

What is contrary to the Spirit? ______________________(v 17)

What else can the Spirit do for you? __________________(v 18)

Read through the things produced by our sinful nature one by one (v 19-21). Are you still doing any of these things? If you are — repent now!

Why is it important not to live this way (v 21)?

____

Write the fruit of the Spirit in the ovals on the tree (v 22-23).

These qualities grow in our lives as we develop as Christians.

❋ John Ch 15: v 1-8

Who is the Vine?

____

Who are the branches?______________

Think!

Am I bearing this fruit of the Spirit in my life? How can I develop more in this way?

Ask other Christians about their experience of the Holy Spirit.

Talking with God

Unit 9

If you wish to get to know someone better, you need to spend time with them, talk with them and share your life with them. So it is with God and *prayer* should spring from our desire to know him better.

Prayer is:
- Being aware of God.
- Sharing with God.
- Talking to God.
- Listening to God.

● I'm sorry Lord ...*Tuning in*

If you want to communicate with God, there must be no blockage between you and him.

What can separate people from God? ______________________________

✱ Luke Ch 18: v 9-14

How should we approach God? ______________________________

If there are things in the way between you and God, tell him about them, say you are sorry, ask for forgiveness and claim his strength for the future. Remember that Jesus died to take away your sins and is risen to give you power for living.

✱ Isaiah Ch 1: v 15-18 Make sure God is listening!

● I love you Lord ...*Worship*

In order to maintain and develop our relationship with God, we should express to him our love, our respect and our trust. The *Psalms* are full of declarations about the goodness and greatness of the Lord.

✱ Psalm 145 (Read alternate verses with your helper or read round.)

How often did David praise the Lord? ______________________(v 2)

What does David say about God?

- ____(v 4-6)
- ____(v 7)
- ____(v 8-9)
- ____(v 11-13)
- ____(v 13b)
- ____(v 14)
- ____(v 18)

As well as the Psalms, there are many other hymns and songs which you can sing in praise to God. As you pray, praise him for his power, his knowledge, his justice, his love. If you run out of words, allow the Holy Spirit to lead you — many have found that speaking and singing in tongues help.

✱ Ephesians Ch 5: v 18-20 **✱ 1 Corinthians Ch 14: v 14-17**

Variety

You can pray **kneeling, sitting, standing or walking** around the room. Christians often **raise their hands, clap, shout, sing and dance** to express their wholehearted love for God. You will often find it helpful to pray aloud, but at other times you may wish to consider **silently** the majesty of God. Be flexible and learn to praise in many ways.

● *I am so grateful Lord* ...*Thanking*

✱ Psalm 100: v 4 **✱ Psalm 147: v 7-9**

Don't forget to thank God for his goodness to you and others.

Give thanks for:
- Food, clothes, home, health, pleasures.
- Family and friends.
- God's blessing on your life and answered prayer.
- Jesus — his life, death and resurrection.

✱ 1 Thessalonians Ch 5: v 16-18

When should we be **joyful?** ______________________________

When should we **pray?** ______________________________

When should we **give thanks?** ______________________________

Our aim should be to walk close to God at all times with grateful and joyful hearts. You can pray secretly to God at any time — at work, at home, in an exam — anywhere!

● *Please Lord*

...Asking

✱ Matthew Ch 6: v 5-15

How shouldn't we pray? ______________________________(v 5)

How should we pray? ______________________________(v 6)

You will find it helpful to *put aside time each day* to spend with God, praying and reading the Bible. Pray in a natural way (v 7) as you would speak to a friend.

Action!

What did Jesus say we should pray for?

- ______________________(v 10)
- ______________________(v 11)
- ______________________(v 12)
- ______________________(v 13)

• *Also pray for:*

- Your family and friends.
- The healing of sick people.
- Those in trouble.
- The people in your church and especially the leaders.
- Those who don't know God — that they might believe.
- Your government (*1 Timothy Ch 2: v 1-4*).

● *Intercession – pleading with God*

There are several occasions in the Bible when people plead with God to change his mind — and indeed he does!

✱ Exodus Ch 32: v 9-14

Like a lawyer in court, Moses presents his case before God. We too can intercede for other people in this way.

✱ Luke Ch 18: v 1-8 *Don't give up – keep praying!*

✱ Colossians Ch 4: v 12-13

How did Epaphras pray? ______________________________

What did he pray? ______________________________

● *Pray in the name of Jesus*

✱ John Ch 16: v 23-24

If we ask in the name of Jesus, we will ______________________

Asking in the name of Jesus is not just tagging words onto the end of a prayer. It is like doing a task in the *name of the King* — we have all the authority of the King behind us to carry out the task. As we pray, we have no righteousness of our own but we come to the Father with all the righteousness and authority of Jesus. The Father hears his Son — so he hears us as we pray in his name!

● *Pray in the power of the Holy Spirit*

Obviously, we need to pray for the things which God wants. We can know the will of God for many things *by reading the Bible,* but we often need to know *how to pray in a particular situation*. The Holy Spirit can help here.

✱ Romans Ch 8: v 26-27

How does the Holy Spirit pray for us?

- ______________________________________(v 26)
- ______________________________________(v 27)

✱ Romans Ch 8: v 34

Who else intercedes for us? ______________________

● *Pray in faith*

✱ James Ch 1: v 5-8 **✱ James Ch 5: v 13-18**

Believe God. Doubt will not bring you answers to prayer. Christians sometimes *fast and pray* for particular things.

● *I'm listening Lord* ...*Two Way*

Our Father

↑ ↓

Us

Prayer should be two way communication. Give God time to speak to you! Wait quietly before him and allow him to lead your thoughts. He may show you that something is wrong in your life, he may tell you to do something or he could lead you to read a part of the Bible.

If God is speaking to you, you should *do what he says*. It is a good idea to *write down* what you feel God is telling you to do. If you are in doubt that it is God speaking, give him more time or talk to someone who can advise you.

Unit 10

Servant of God

Before you became a Christian, you were a slave of sin, your human nature, and Satan. They were hard taskmasters who ruled your life. Now, by the kindness of God, you are *free* of those things and have *chosen to serve God*. Your *new boss* will be able to help you as long as you submit to him and obey him.

Your new boss will make demands on you — in fact he asks for your whole life!

✱ Matthew Ch 16: v 24-28

What must we do to follow Jesus? ______________________________

____(v 24)

What must you do to save and find your life?

____(v 25)

But God is not a hard taskmaster. We are his children as well as his servants and the choice is always ours to serve him or not. We need to trust his promises that serving him is the *best way of life now* and will lead to *eternal life in the future.*

✱ John Ch 14: v 15

Why do we obey Jesus? ______________________________

✱ John Ch 15: v 9-13

Who is our example of obedience? __________________________(v 10)

What is the result of obedience? __________________________(v 11)

What is the command of Jesus? __________________________(v 12)

____

Finding joy

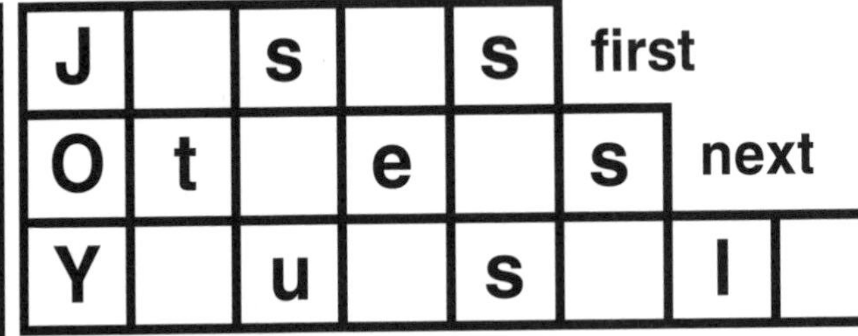

Living sacrifices

✱ Romans Ch 12: v 1-2

What can you offer as a living sacrifice? ______________________

A sacrifice used to be a valuable thing (eg a lamb) given to God as part of worship. We are asked to give our bodies to God for him to use during our lives. We are no longer our own, *we belong to God.* He has plans for us in his Kingdom which can only be fulfilled as we yield ourselves to him so that *we are his instruments* here on earth.

What should we *not conform* to? ______________________

____

As Christians, we expect to be different from those around us — we belong to a different Kingdom!

How are we *transformed*? ______________________

As the Holy Spirit guides us, our whole way of thinking can be changed so that we are in tune with the will of God.

Using time wisely

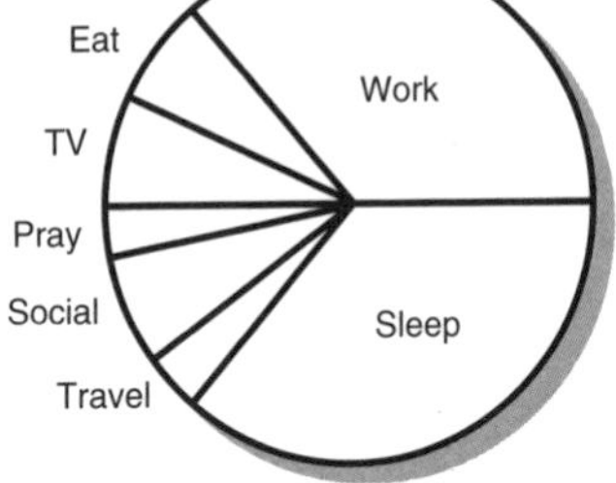

✱ Psalm 31: v 14-15

I trust in you, O Lord; I say ______________________

My times are ______________________

✱ Ephesians Ch 5: v 15-17

How should we use our time?

____

____

How do you spend your time?

✱ Ecclesiastes Ch 3: v 1-8

✱ 1 Corinthians Ch 6: v 19-20

What is your body? ______________________________

Think!

Is Jesus Lord of my life?

• Work, college, school

Do I take God to work with me — Do I ask God to guide me at work — Am I prepared to stay where I am or move jobs if God tells me to — Am I honest in my dealings at work — How do I treat my boss and others at work — Do I gossip behind people's backs?

• Home, family

Is God in my family life — How do I treat my parents, brothers, sisters, children, husband, wife — Do I love them and pray for them — Am I helpful at home and do I live for Jesus and bring happiness — Am I bad tempered and difficult to live with?

• Recreation, interests

Have I ever prayed about my interests and activities — Are they all appropriate for a Christian — Do I waste time, watch too much TV, drink too much etc?

• Friendships, relationships

How am I with my friends — Do I listen as well as talk — Do I think about their needs and give practical help — Do I forgive and say sorry when things get strained — Have I asked God about my boyfriend/girlfriend?

• Sex

Do I have a clear conscience before God in this area of my life — Am I happy that God is watching all that I do?

• Money, possessions

Have I said to God "All that I have is yours, Lord" — Am I selfish with the things that I have — Do I consider myself as a steward of God's things — Do I pray about my giving to others and the work of God — Am I impulsive when I go shopping — Do I pray before I buy — Am I living within my means — Am I sliding into debt — Am I honest in all my financial dealings?

• Prayer and Bible study

Do I spend enough time alone with God or is he getting squeezed out of my life?

• Thoughts

Are my thoughts under the control of God?

If he is not <u>Lord of all</u>, he is not really <u>Lord at all</u>!

Obedience to God can mean obedience to others

Acts Ch 5: v 29	
Heb Ch 13 v 7, 17	
Rom Ch 13: v 1-7	
Eph Ch 5: v 21	
Eph Ch 5 v 22-24	
Eph Ch 6: v 1-3	
Eph Ch 6: v 5-8	

Finding the will of God

The Holy Spirit can speak to you through a number of different channels — here are some of them — listen to them all!

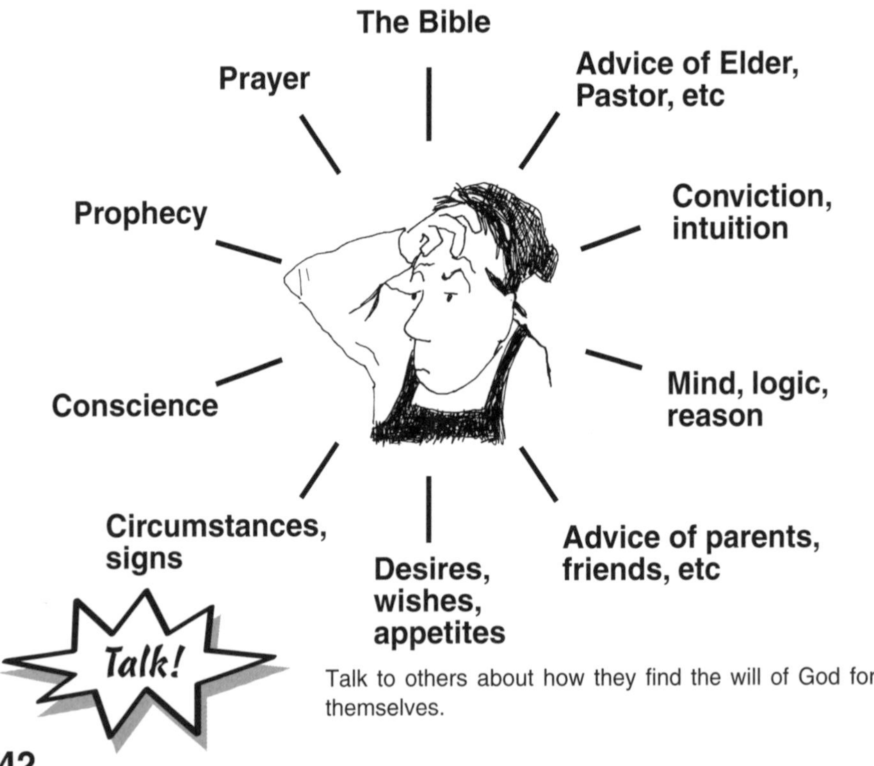

Talk to others about how they find the will of God for themselves.

Know the Enemy

Unit 11

● Satan – who is he?

Extra Bible study

- ✻ **Genesis Ch 3**
- ✻ **Luke Ch 10: v 18**
- ✻ **Revelation Ch 12: v 7-9**
- ✻ **Job Ch 1-2**
- ✻ **Isaiah Ch 14: v 12-15**
- ✻ **Ezekiel Ch 28: v 12-19**

From beginning to end, the Bible takes for granted the existence of Satan. He is a *personal*, spiritual being who is the *source of evil* in the world and he is bitterly opposed to the purposes of God.

We have no detailed account of where he came from but there are a few clues (see extra Bible study). It seems that he was a responsible angel who was filled with pride and rebelled against God with a number of other angels (these became demons). **His power is not equal to that of God** and he can only operate by the permission of God.

✻ Revelation Ch 12: v 9 What *four* descriptions are given here?

- ____________________
- ____________________
- ____________________
- ____________________

✻ John Ch 8: v 42-47

If God is your Father, what is your attitude to Jesus?

____(v 42)

Who is the father of those who do not hear or believe in Jesus? ________

Find two characteristics of the devil (v 44).

- ____________________
- ____________________

✻ 1 Peter Ch 5: v 8-9 What else is the devil like?

____

● *What does Satan do?*

Gen Ch 3: v 13	
Luke Ch 4: v 1-2	
Luke Ch 8: v 12	
Luke Ch 13: v 16	
Acts Ch 5: v 3	
1 Thess Ch 2: v 17-18	

✱ 2 Corinthians Ch 11: v 14

How does Satan disguise himself? ____________________

There is no doubt that Satan is unhappy that you have changed your allegiance and have become a follower of Jesus. He will do all he can to *deceive you, destroy your faith, lead you into sin and spoil your life*. As Christians, we are in a battle, but we need not fear since we have all the resources of God at our disposal.

✱ Colossians Ch 1: v 13

What has God rescued you from? ____________________

What has he brought you into? ____________________

● *Satan is defeated*

✱ 1 John Ch 3: v 8

Whom are we following when we sin? ____________________

Why did Jesus come? ____________________

✱ Hebrews Ch 2: v 14

How did Jesus overcome the devil? ____________________

In a war there is often a *decisive battle* which makes the outcome of the war certain. Our decisive battle was won by Jesus on the cross. The devil is around at the moment and we are engaged in skirmishes but we are on the victory side. Satan's days are numbered and eventually he will be destroyed (*Revelation Ch 20: v 10*).

● *'Supernatural' – from God or the devil?*

✱ Deuteronomy Ch 13: v 1-3

How do we distinguish the true prophet from the false prophet?

____

✱ Deuteronomy Ch 18: v 9-14

Write down some of the forbidden activities mentioned here:

____

____

What does God think of them? ______________________

Everybody has a *spiritual void* in their lives which should be filled with the things of God. Satan offers poor substitutes to fill the gap and so people try to find satisfaction in the occult, religion, philosophy, art, sex etc. In some of these areas men and women are dangerously exposed to Satanic and demonic activity.

Some areas of demonic activity

Meditation

- Transcendental Meditation
- Astral Projection
- Hypnotism
- Yoga
- Religions & cults

Fortune telling

- Horoscopes
- Astrology
- Tarot cards
- Crystal balls
- Mirror mantics
- Palm reading
- Tea leaves

Magic

- Casting spells
- Wearing charms
- Black/White magic
- Satanism
- Witchcraft
- Halloween

Psychic phenomena

- Ouija boards
- Occult games
- Levitation
- Extra Sensory Perception
- Clairvoyance
- Clairaudience
- Water divining
- Seances
- Spiritism
- Spiritualist healing

Other possible areas

- Occult books
- Occult plays and films
- Music by occult groups
- Horror films
- Some science fiction
- Effect of drugs
- Fairy stories & fantasy
- Sexual perversion
- Martial arts
- Emotional problems

● *What if I have been involved in dangerous areas?*

Have you ever been involved in these activities? The list is not complete — allow the Holy Spirit to bring to mind any other areas.

• *Repent*

Make no excuses. Tell God that you are sorry for your involvement. Admit that you were wrong. Ask God for forgiveness — remember *1 John Ch 1: v 9*. You need have no fear. Forgive those who have wronged you.

• *Renounce*

Clearly state *to the enemy* that you have left his province and now belong to God. Tell Satan that you break any previous contracts!

❋ James Ch 4: v 7

Whom do we submit to? ______________________________

Whom do we resist? ______________________________

What will the devil do?____________________

• *Destroy*

Destroy all objects connected with the occult. It may mean getting rid of charms, books, pictures, statues, letters, discs, media, music, horoscopes, masks etc.

❋ Acts Ch 19: v 18-19

What did these Ephesians destroy? ______________________

...If in doubt, throw it out!

• *Break*

Break all contact with these activities. This might mean seeing less of certain friends etc. Pray much and seek the will of God in the matter.

• *Be filled with the Holy Spirit*

❋ Matthew Ch 12: v 43-45 Don't leave yourself empty!

Some people who have been involved in these dangerous areas need special help and deliverance. Don't be afraid to talk with your church leaders if you think that you have problems.

Some symptoms of possible demonic involvement

- Prolonged deep depression
- Fits of temper and violence
- Irrational fears
- Obsessive suicidal thoughts
- Blasphemous thoughts
- Evil dreams
- Fascination with sex, pornography
- Some illnesses
- Hate, fear, rejection, jealousy
- Addictions

Victory in Jesus

Unit 12

✱ Ephesians Ch 6: v 10-18

What must we put on? ________________________________ (v 11)

Who is not our enemy? ________________________________ (v 12)

Who is our enemy? ________________________________

________________________________ (v 11-12)

● Aiming at the right enemy

As Christians we should never treat other people as enemies. They may be wicked, evil and involved in all kinds of sin. They may abuse us, persecute us and be thoroughly unpleasant to us. Our response should always be to *love others as God loves them*.

We must hate sin but love the sinner

Our attack should be aimed at the evil forces influencing the lives of others and ourselves — it is spiritual warfare.

Why must we put our armour on?

________________________________ (v 13)

Beware of the enemy's arsenal!

- ✱ **Disease**
- ✱ **Disaster**
- ✱ **Despair**

D - Bombs

- ✱ **Doubt**
- ✱ **Depression**
- ✱ **Disappointment**
- ✱ **Disunity**
- ✱ **Disillusionment**
- ✱ **Distress**
- ✱ **Discouragement**

Can you think of any more D-Bombs?

Righteousness

You cannot expect to live powerfully for God if you harbour sin in your life — it is a chink in your armour that the enemy can easily penetrate and make you ineffective. Repent and receive the righteousness which God gives you.

Prayer

This is your *communication with headquarters*. Make sure that you are carrying out your commander's instructions. If you rely on your own tactics and methods, you will fail — find the will of God and obey him.

Faith, salvation and truth

The enemy will try all sorts of ways to sow doubt in your mind and draw you away from God. Look out for the *flaming arrows*:

Resist with **faith** in the character of God. He is good, just, loving, holy, pure, powerful, the creator and he knows everything (*Psalm 92*).

Be assured of your **salvation**. Say to the enemy "I am a child of God, God has a purpose for my life, I am saved, God will provide all the strength I need to live for him" (*Romans Ch 8: v 28-39*).

Remember that your enemy is a liar — rebuke him with the **truth** of God's word. Also as we are *honest and truthful* in all we do and say, we will foil the plots of the enemy.

● *The Word of God and the gospel*

The Word of God is a powerful weapon against the enemy:

Read the Word ... Learn the Word ... Use the Word

● *Overcoming temptation*

✱ Luke Ch 4: v 1-12

What were Jesus' three temptations?

- ____________________
- ____________________
- ____________________

How did Jesus defend himself each time?

____________________(v 4, 8, 12)

(See *Deuteronomy Ch 8: v 3, Ch 6: v 13, 16*)

✱ Hebrews Ch 4: v 14-16

Who is our great high priest?____________________

Why is he able to sympathise with our weaknesses?

____

How is he different from us? ____________________(v 15)

What are we promised in time of need?

____________________(v 16)

Jesus was a *real man* and the temptations which he faced were just as real as ours. He can give us power to overcome because he overcame and we possess the same Spirit which was in Jesus (*Romans Ch 8: v 11*).

Temptations can come in many areas of our lives. Satan uses circumstances, our bodily desires, our thoughts and other people to bring temptation. We can be tempted to do wrong things and we can be tempted not to do things which are right.

- ***What are your main temptations?***
- ______________________________
- ______________________________

Think!

Temptation is not sin

✱ James Ch 1: v 12-18

A temptation is just the first thought or inclination towards sin. What we do with that first thought is critical! If we allow it to develop then it becomes sinful thinking and can lead to sinful actions.

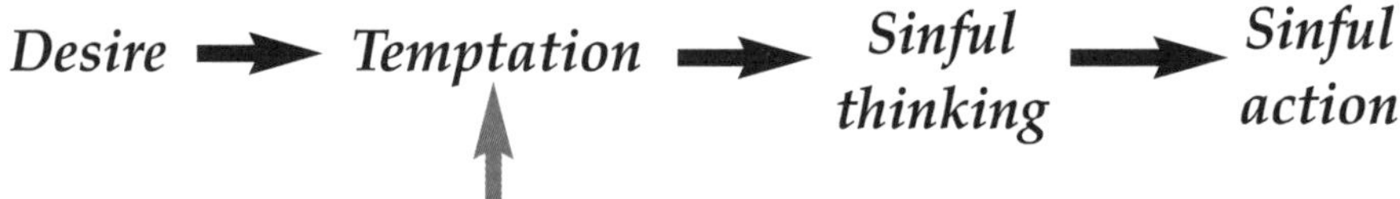

You need to take hold of the power of God and reject the temptation before it has developed into sin. Use your weapons of warfare! If you do sin in thought or action then you must repent — ask God to forgive you and ask him for power to overcome in the future.

What does God give to us?

______________________________(v 17)

✱ 1 Corinthians Ch 10: v 13

Are your particular temptations unusual? ____________

Does God permit you to be tempted beyond your strength? ______

What does God provide with *every* temptation?

____

Avoid

When a soldier fights, part of his defence is *evasive action* — moving out of the main line of fire of the enemy. We should not put ourselves unnecessarily into situations where we will be strongly tempted. Sometimes it means avoiding certain places, people, literature, music etc. We should be very careful in situations where we know we have failed in the past.

Look at the temptations you have written above - is there some evasive action which you can take?

Unit 13

The Church

A big world-wide family

As a Christian, you belong to a large family. You will find that you quickly feel one with your "brothers" and "sisters" in Christ, even though you may come from different cultures and backgrounds.

The true church

There are many "Christian" organisations, denominations and movements. Belonging to one of these does not automatically make you a Christian and you may find a mixture of believers and non-believers in these organisations. The *true church* is all those people on earth who are truly born again — who have *repented,* who have *faith* in Jesus as their personal Saviour, who own *Jesus as their Lord* and who have a *relationship with God*. Only God can see his full strategy involving his people all over the world.

A local church

A local church is a group of Christians united in beliefs, aims and purpose, working together for God in an area. It is essential for every Christian to become part of a local church.

Look up the verses in *Ephesians* and connect with the description of the church given below.

Eph Ch 2: v 19-20 •	• ***The bride of Christ***
Eph Ch 2: v 21-22 •	• ***An army***
Eph Ch 4: v 15-16 •	• ***God's people - a household***
Eph Ch 5: v 22-32 •	• ***People in which God lives***
Eph Ch 6: v 10-18 •	• ***The body of Christ***

The body of Christ

The church is an *organism,* not just an organisation. It is built on *relationships* between God and man and between people. Church membership is only meaningful with the love, trust and commitment which Jesus talked about.

✱ John Ch 13: v 34-35

How are the disciples of Jesus recognised? ______________________

✱ 1 Corinthians Ch 12: v 12-26

Here Paul compares the church with a human body. The members of the church are like the parts of the body.

Notice the following:

- We are all parts of the *same body* (v 12).
- We all *belong* to the body (v 14-16).
- We have *different gifts* and functions (v 14-19).
- *Variety* is a strength (v 17).
- We all *need each other* to be complete (v 21).
- Every member is *important* (v 22-25).
- We *share* in each other's sufferings and joys (v 26).

This is why it is important to become part of a church so that you can find your gifts and function in the local body of Christ. *You need your brothers and sisters and they need you.* You will find that other Christians are quite different from yourself but this can be a strength as you pull together and grow in your service and knowledge of God.

Gifts

The church can continue the work of Jesus here on earth as you participate with the gifts that God has given to you. These gifts are given for the building up of the body of Christ so that it can be effective for God. Read again the list of gifts in *1 Corinthians Ch 12: v 8-10.*

✱ Romans Ch 12: v 3-8 Find *seven* gifts

Do you have any of these gifts?

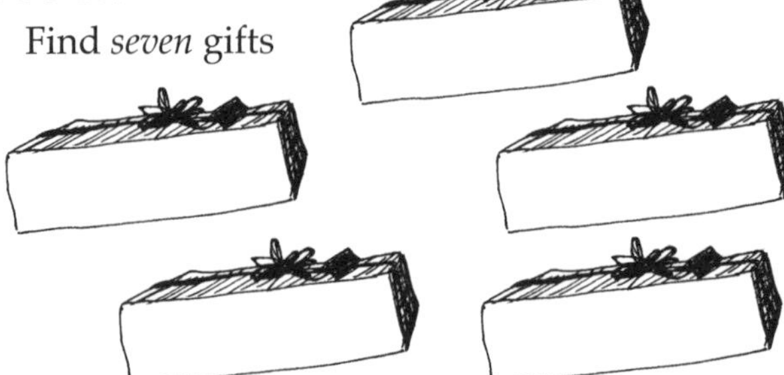

● Ministry gifts

✱ Ephesians Ch 4: v 11-13

Certain people will emerge with prominent recognised gifts.

Ministry gift	*Description*	*People with gifts*
	Church planter and builder sent out from his home church.	Rom 1:1, 1 Peter 1:1
	Brings the counsel of God to specific situations, visionary.	Acts 15:32, Acts 21:10
	Preaches the gospel. People come to faith, healed, delivered.	Acts 8:4-7, Acts 21:8
	Leads and cares for the people, a shepherd.	John 21:15-17
	Understands the word of God and is able to faithfully pass on the truth to others.	1 Cor 4:17, 1 Tim 4:11-16

Why are these five ministry gifts given to the church?

____

____

You might know people in your church with these ministries. Some may give up their secular work to serve God with their gifts.

● Leaders in the church

In New Testament times, a local church was led by *elders* or *overseers*. Paul appointed leaders in the churches which he planted or he delegated the task to others.

✱ 1 Timothy Ch 3: v 1-7 **✱ Titus Ch 1: v 5-9**

What qualities was Paul looking for in leaders?

• ________	• ________	• ________
• ________	• ________	• ________
• ________	• ________	• ________
• ________	• ________	• ________
• ________	• ________	• ________
• ________	• ________	• ________

You will see that most of these are *character qualities*.

✱ Hebrews Ch 13: v 17

Why must leaders take their task seriously?

___

Why should you obey your leaders and submit to them?

___

● *Fellowship*

✱ 1 John Ch 1: v 3, 7

Whom is our fellowship with? • ___

• ___ • ___

Fellowship with other Christians is more than just friendship, it is participating together in God and sharing with each other.

✱ Acts 2: v 42-47

- **Being together (v 42, 44, 46)** — In order to operate as one body, we must spend time together. There may be large meetings, small meetings, formal or informal or it may be just having a meal together and encouraging each other. Make sure that you are benefitting from all the God-given gifts in your church. Don't neglect meeting together but let us encourage one another (*Hebrews Ch 10: v 25*).
- **Sharing lives** — As Christians, we need to learn to trust each other. This involves being open and honest without pretence. It means being yourself and sharing your joys, sorrows and fears. It means caring, understanding and not judging.
- **Sharing possessions and money (v 44, 45)** — From earliest times, Christians have shared their possessions. Learn to share your house, car, gadgets, books, food etc with your brothers and sisters - we own nothing, we are only stewards of God's property. Many Christians give a tenth of their income (a "tithe") to the work of God — particularly in their local church *(2 Corinthians Ch 9: v 6-8).*
- **Working together (v 47)** — Find out what the aims and vision of your church are and get involved in what is going on. There is much work to do in the Kingdom of God!

✱ Ephesians Ch 5: v 23

Who is the Head of the church?

___

How involved are you in your local church? What can you do to get more involved?

The Future

Unit 14

✱ Acts Ch 1: v 6-11

Ever since Jesus was taken up into heaven, Christians have been expecting him to return as he promised. It might seem that he is taking a long time about it! How many years ago did Jesus ascend to heaven (about AD 30)? ____________________

✱ 2 Peter Ch 3: v 8-9

Why is the Lord waiting? ____________________

____

● Signs of the end

✱ Matthew Ch 24: v 3-14

The disciples asked Jesus about the sign of *his coming* and of *the end of the age*. Find some of the signs:

F _ _ _ _ C _ _ _ _ _ _ _ _ (v 4-5, 24)

W _ _ _ (v 6-7) F _ _ _ _ _ _ _ _ (v 7)

E _ _ _ _ _ _ _ _ _ _ _ _ _ _ (v 7)

P _ _ _ _ _ _ _ _ _ _ _ _ _ _ (v 9-10)

F _ _ _ _ P _ _ _ _ _ _ _ _ _ _ (v 11, 24)

G _ _ _ _ _ _ P _ _ _ _ _ _ _ _ _ _ (v 14)

Which of these signs can you see in the world today?

The Bible speaks of increasing sin and unpleasantness on this earth culminating in political, social, economic and religious unity under the reign of an evil dictator sometimes called the "Anti-Christ".

✱ 2 Thessalonians Ch 2: v 1-12

Who must be revealed before Jesus returns?

______________________________(v 3)

Who does this person claim to be? ______________________________(v 4)

Who is behind this person? ______________________________(v 9)

What will Jesus do when he returns? ______________________________(v 8)

● *What happens when Jesus comes back?*

✱ 1 Thessalonians Ch 4: v 13-18

Why does the rest of mankind grieve about those who die?

______________________________(v 13)

Why can we be confident that Christians will rise from the dead?

______________________________(v 14)

How will the Lord come from heaven?

______________________________(v 16)

Christians who have died (the "dead in Christ") will be raised from the dead first and then the living Christians will also be taken up to be with the Lord.

How long will we be with the Lord? ______________________________(v 17)

This is the confidence and joy that we have because Jesus has saved us!

● *A new body*

✱ 1 Corinthians Ch 15: v 42-57

When Jesus returns, we will be given a new body fit for our eternal life with God. Compare your old and new bodies:

verse	*Your body now*	*Your resurrection body*
42	sown	raised
43	sown	raised
43	sown	raised
44	sown	raised

Whose is our earthly body like? ________________________________(v 45-47)

Whose is our new body like? __________________________________(v 48-49)

Why do Christians not need to fear death (v 50-57)?

Think!

● When will Jesus return?

✱ Matthew Ch 24: v 36-44

Who is the only one who knows the time of the end? ____________(v 36)

When will Jesus return? ____(v 44)

What *two* things must we do?

• ____________________________(v 42) • ____________________________(v 44)

Action!

How can I do these two things?

____

____

● What about judgment?

The judgment of God will be *entirely just* and based on *man's response to the will of God*. It will take into account our actions, thoughts, attitudes, words, faith, knowledge and abilities.

● Saved or lost – heaven or hell?

The Bible speaks many times of a final separation of good and evil, a time when the destinies of men will be decided.

✱ Matthew Ch 13: v 24-30, 36-43

Who are the good seed? ____(v 38)

Who are the weeds? ____(v 38)

Who is the Son of Man? ____(v 41)

What is the fate of evil people? ______________________________(v 42)

What will happen to the righteous? ____________________________

____(v 43)

✱ Romans Ch 14: v 10-12

Who will appear before God's judgment seat? ____________________

You may be worried that you are not good enough and that you will end up in hell. Actually, *nobody is good enough* (*Romans Ch 3: v 23*) and if we stood alone with our own lives before God, we would all be lost. This is why Jesus came to exchange his perfect life for our sin.

✱ Romans Ch 3: v 21-26

Whom does our righteousness come from? ____________________(v 22)

What must we have in order to receive righteousness?

____(v 22)

What did Jesus do to give us righteousness?

____(v 25)

Faith  Jesus gave us his righteousness ← → Jesus took our sins

Three important words

Justified	"Just-as-if-I" had never sinned. If you are justified in court, you are no longer guilty and can walk out free.
Grace	**G**od's **R**iches **A**t **C**hrist's **E**xpense. Grace is an unearned, undeserved gift (Ephesians Ch 2: v 8-9).
Redemption	Setting free. A slave is redeemed when his freedom is paid for. Jesus paid the price on the cross to set us free from sin and its consequences.

● *Grand finale*

✱ Revelation Ch 20: v 11-15

Those who are not saved by faith in Christ will also rise from the dead and stand before God's throne. They will not be saved by their deeds and they will be lost.

✱ Revelation Ch 21: v 1-4 **✱ Revelation Ch 22: v 1-5**

This is your eternal life — life without sorrow, crying, pain, darkness or death. There will be joy, gladness and light in the presence of God. Hallelujah!

Fishers of Men

Unit 15

✱ Mark Ch 1: v 14-20

Which four disciples of Jesus started off as fishermen and ended up fishing for men?

• ______________ • ______________ • ______________ • ______________

Christians have always been enthusiastic to share their faith with others. Over the centuries they have been persecuted, tortured and even killed because of their insistence that the good news is for the whole world.

✱ Acts Ch 12: v 1-4

Which of the above did Herod execute? ______________________________

● Why should we tell others about Jesus?

...because Jesus told us to

✱ Luke Ch 24: v 45-49

What was the message to be preached to all nations?

____

A witness is someone who tells others about what they have seen or experienced. Every Christian is called to be a witness to their experience of God and the truth of the gospel.

What do we need to be effective witnesses? ____________________(v 49)

✱ Matthew Ch 5: v 14-16

Our witness is not just words, it is actions too. What will people do when they see our good deeds?

____

Let your light shine!

● Why should we tell others about Jesus?

...because Jesus has died

God has shown his great love for mankind in sending Jesus and allowing him to die for the sins of the world. God is a loving Father waiting for people to repent and turn to him.

✱ 2 Corinthians Ch 5: v 17-21

What message do we have? ________________________________(v 19)

What are we? ____(v 20)

Embassy staff! — we are representatives for the Kingdom of God among the people we meet day by day.

How should we speak to people?

• _______________________(v 20) • _______________________(v 11)

What drives us on? ____(v 14)

● Why should we tell others about Jesus?

...because people are lost without God

✱ John Ch 3: v 16-18

Who are condemned? ____

✱ John 14: v 6

Are there other ways to God apart from Jesus? _____________________

✱ Ezekiel Ch 3: v 16-19

Since we are aware of the plight of our fellow men, it is our responsibility to *warn* them of the danger they are in.

✱ Matthew Ch 10: v 32-33

● Why should we tell others about Jesus?

...because Jesus offers a better life now

✱ John Ch 10: v 10

Why did Jesus come? ____

____

Jesus offers peace, joy, happiness, deliverance, healing, provision ... and more! We have *good news* to share with our friends.

● Being ready to share the good news

- **Pray** for your friends, family, workmates, etc — that God will speak to them.
- **Pray** for *opportunities* to talk to people about Jesus. Look for these "divine appointments" as they arise and allow the Holy Spirit to lead you in conversation.

✱ 1 Peter Ch 3: v 13-17

We can expect opposition as we stand up for what is right and share about Jesus.

We should not ________________________________ (v 14)

We should always be ____________________________ (v 15)

How should we share the good news?

with ______________________________________ (v 15-16)

● How can I tell others about Jesus?

...say what God has done in your life

This is sometimes called "giving your testimony". People will often be interested in what you have to say about:

- **Before** — My life before I became a Christian.
- **How** — How, when, where and why I became a Christian.
- **Since** — The difference Christ is making in my life.

✱ Acts Ch 26: v 1-29

Read Paul's testimony. Can you see the *before, how and since*?

Now talk about your before, how and since with someone.

You can also tell your friends about your church and what God is doing in the lives of people known to you. Share about how people have been saved, healed, delivered etc.

● How can I tell others about Jesus?

...know what you believe and be able to explain it

- Try to avoid too much religious language and jargon — explain unfamiliar words as you talk.
- Use the Bible to back up what you are saying.

Useful verses

Underline these verses in your Bible, learn them and keep a note of them in the cover of your Bible.

Five doublets

The problem	Isaiah	53:6	&	59:2	Sin separates
	Romans	3:23	&	6:23	Sin's penalty
God's remedy	1 Peter	2:24	&	3:18	Jesus died for us
Our response	Acts	2:38	&	3:19	Repent
	John	1:12	&	3:16	Believe and receive

Useful passages

Acts	10:34-43	Summary of the life and work of Jesus.
Luke	15:11-32	Parable of the lost son.
John	3:1-21	Be born again.
Psalm	103	God's love, compassion and forgiveness.

- Invite your friends to events where they will meet other Christians and hear the good news presented in a clear and relevant way.
- Give them books, booklets, leaflets, CDs, DVDs, web links, files, apps or the Bible so that they can think about things further on their own.

● How can I tell others about Jesus?

...be prepared to lead your friend to Christ

If your friend is ready, encourage them to pray aloud preferably in their own words or following you. Don't be afraid to guide or prompt, they will probably never have prayed aloud before!

Make sure that they:

- Repent and renounce sin (be specific if necessary).
- Thank Jesus for dying for them, ask for forgiveness and cleansing.
- Invite Jesus into their life to be lord, master and friend.

● Follow-up

Make sure that they get linked up to a church where they will be looked after in their Christian life. Encourage them to read the Bible, pray and to be led by the Holy Spirit. Pray for them yourself.

You may wish to go through ***First Steps*** with them!

My story

(Use this and the next page to write about your own Christian experience.)

My story (continued)

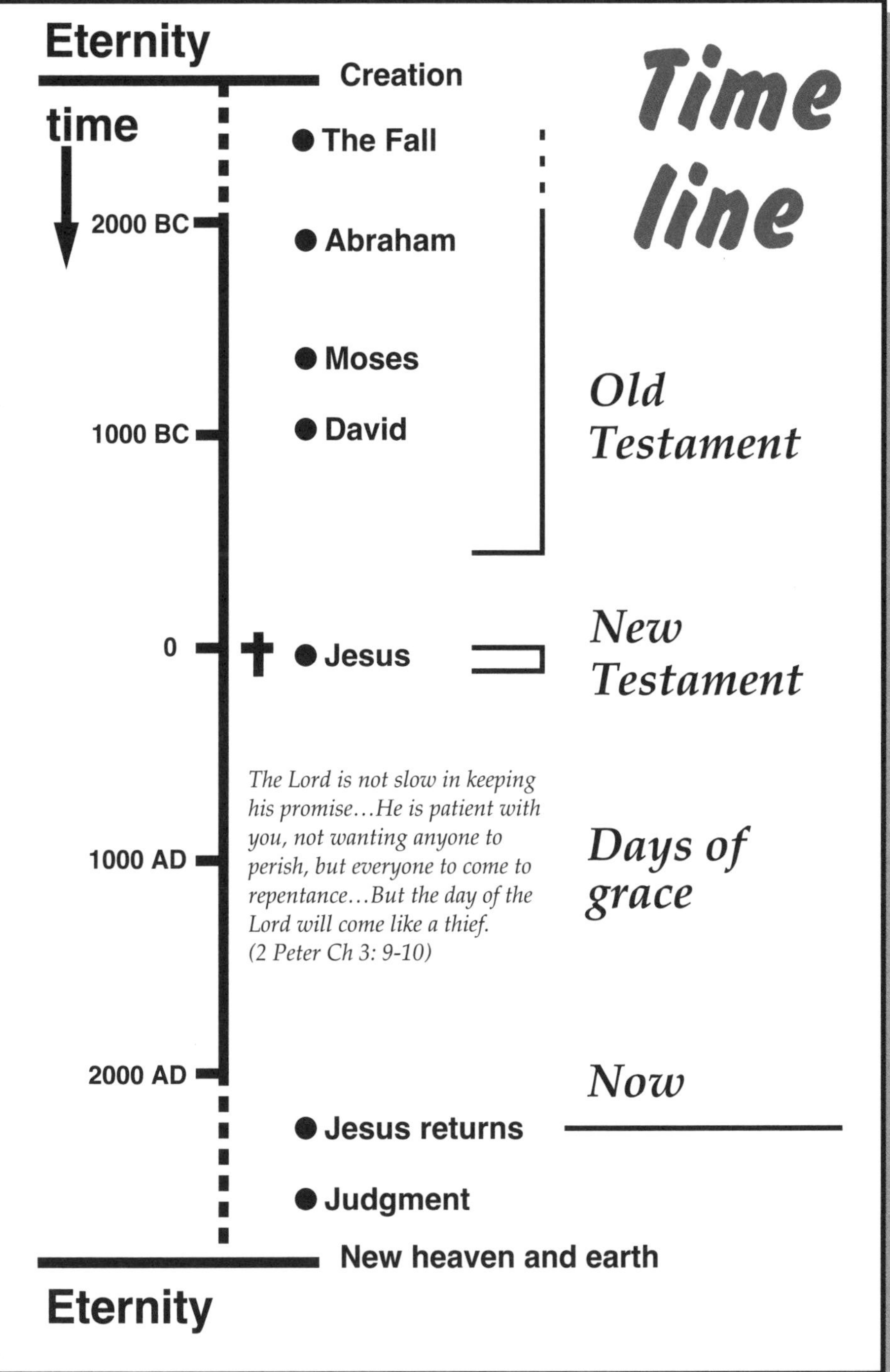
Eternity
Creation
Time line
time
The Fall
2000 BC
Abraham
Moses
Old Testament
1000 BC
David
0
Jesus
New Testament
The Lord is not slow in keeping his promise…He is patient with you, not wanting anyone to perish, but everyone to come to repentance…But the day of the Lord will come like a thief.
(2 Peter Ch 3: 9-10)
1000 AD
Days of grace
2000 AD
Now
Jesus returns
Judgment
New heaven and earth
Eternity

Old Testament survey

• *Origins*

The first eleven chapters of the Bible cover the origins of the universe, the world and the human race. The wonderful account of the creation of mankind is followed by the tragic entry of sin into humanity through Adam and Eve. The spread of wickedness was such that God found it necessary to bring judgment by a flood and by confusion of languages.

• *Abraham — Covenant of promise and faith*

God made a covenant with Abraham promising various things about his descendants: they would become a large nation who would possess the land of Israel — they would have a special relationship with God who would bless them — and they would be a blessing to the other nations of the world particularly through one descendant. Abraham is the spiritual father of those who have faith. Abraham's grandson, Jacob, changed his name to Israel and his sons gave rise to the 12 tribes of Israel. These developed into a nation over 400 years in Egypt (around 1700 - 1300 BC) where they became slaves.

• *Moses — Covenant of law*

Under Moses the Israelites escaped miraculously from Egypt. God appeared dramatically to Moses and gave him the 10 commandments and many other laws and instructions about worship and sacrifice. After 40 years wandering in the desert, Joshua led the people into the promised land where they settled.

• *David — Covenant of kingdom*

After a period of rule by judges, Samuel appointed Saul as the first king of Israel. David succeeded him and established the kingdom of Israel and Jerusalem as the capital city. God made a covenant with David that his kingdom would last for ever. David's son, Solomon, built a magnificent temple in Jerusalem but after his death the kingdom was divided into the northern kingdom of 'Israel' (10 tribes) with its capital in Samaria and the southern kingdom of 'Judah' (2 tribes) which retained Jerusalem as its capital.

• *Exile*

Following a succession of bad kings, the northern kingdom of Israel was defeated by the Assyrians in 722 BC and the ten tribes were deported and lost. The southern kingdom of Judah had some good kings and lasted longer but eventually fell to the Babylonians in 587 BC. A large proportion of the population (including Ezekiel and Daniel) was deported to Babylon for 70 years in exile.

• *Restoration*

After the Babylonians were defeated by the Persians, the Jews (from the word Judah) gradually returned to the land of Israel and restored their national life. They rebuilt a smaller version of the temple, repaired the walls of Jerusalem and reinstated the law of Moses under Zerubbabel, Nehemiah and Ezra. They continued to be dominated by larger foreign powers (Greece, Egypt and Syria) until the Roman Empire enveloped the land of Israel around 63 BC.

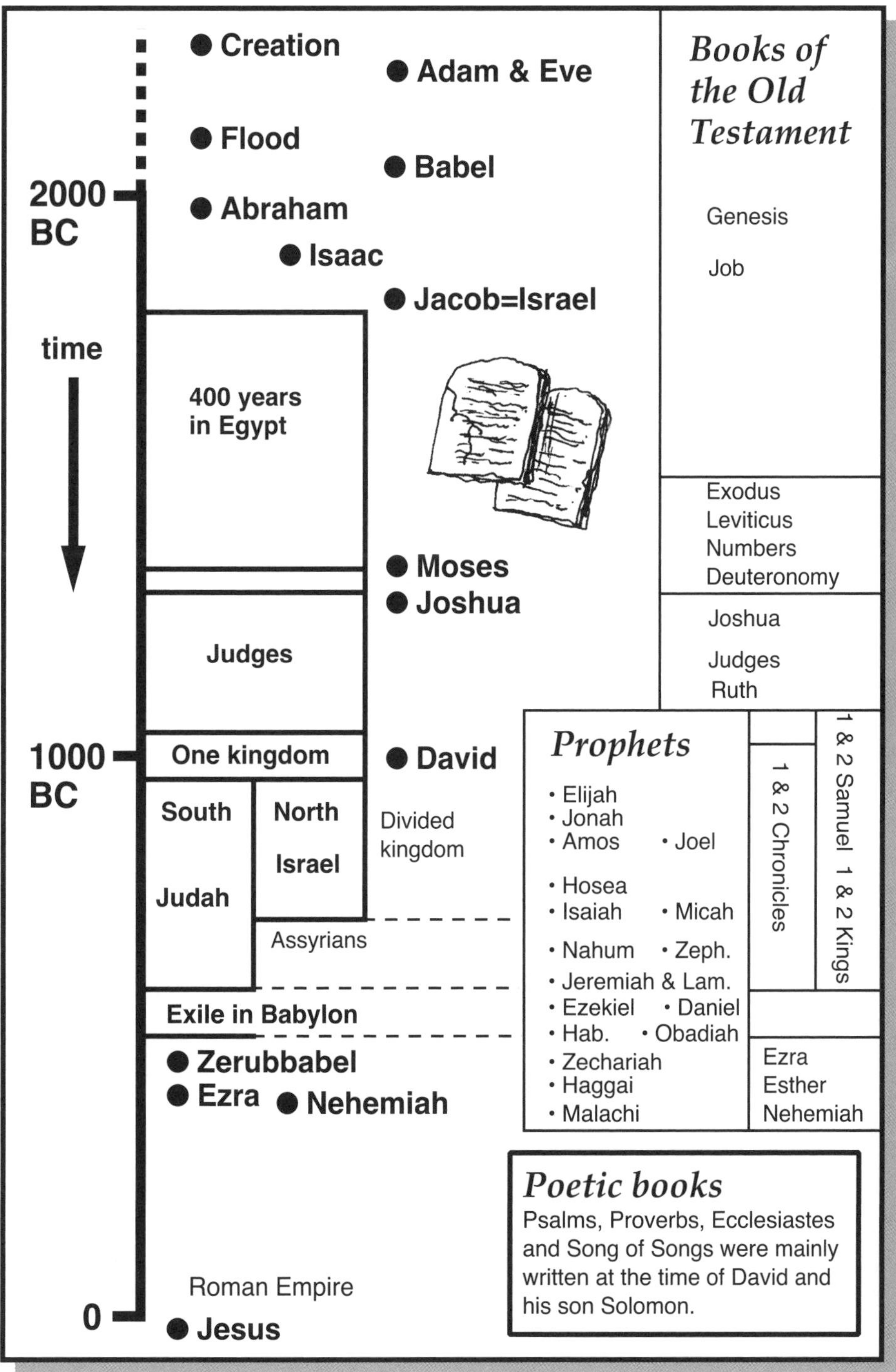
Creation
Adam & Eve
Flood
Babel
2000 BC
Abraham
Isaac
Jacob=Israel
time
400 years in Egypt
Moses
Joshua
Judges
1000 BC
One kingdom
David
South
Judah
North
Israel
Divided kingdom
Assyrians
Exile in Babylon
Zerubbabel
Ezra
Nehemiah
Roman Empire
0
Jesus
Books of the Old Testament
Genesis
Job
Exodus
Leviticus
Numbers
Deuteronomy
Joshua
Judges
Ruth
Prophets
• Elijah
• Jonah
• Amos
• Joel
• Hosea
• Isaiah
• Micah
• Nahum
• Zeph.
• Jeremiah & Lam.
• Ezekiel
• Daniel
• Hab.
• Obadiah
• Zechariah
• Haggai
• Malachi
1 & 2 Chronicles
1 & 2 Samuel 1 & 2 Kings
Ezra
Esther
Nehemiah
Poetic books
Psalms, Proverbs, Ecclesiastes and Song of Songs were mainly written at the time of David and his son Solomon.

New Testament survey

• *Background*

The events of the New Testament take place in the first 70 years AD. The land of Israel was under Roman rule and Pontius Pilate was the Roman governor at one stage. Rule was also delegated to a Jewish family, the Herods, who supervised the building of a massive temple in Jerusalem. The main religious leaders were the priests, pharisees, sadducees and scribes. The Jews were looking for a Messiah-king who would rescue them from foreign rulers and establish a universal and everlasting kingdom modelled on the great days of the kingdom of David.

• *Jesus of Nazareth*

Jesus' mother, Mary from Nazareth, became pregnant supernaturally by the Holy Spirit. At the time of his birth there was a census and Mary and Joseph were at their home town of Bethlehem to be registered (Jesus was a descendant of King David who also came from Bethlehem about 1000 years before). Apart from a brief incident at 12 years old, we know little about the first 30 years of Jesus' life — he probably worked with his father, Joseph, as a carpenter and had some form of education.

• *Jesus — his ministry*

At about 30 years old, Jesus was baptised by John the Baptist and was tempted during a long fast in the desert. Then began two or three years of travelling, preaching and healing around the land of Israel. His message was radical — he preached about a kingdom but it was not a political kingdom, it was the Kingdom of God, a Kingdom not of this world. He concentrated on caring for needy individuals, healing and restoring dignity. He cut through the hypocrisy of the religious leaders and exposed their inconsistencies. He demonstrated his spiritual authority by casting demons out of people and performing miracles. He claimed to be the Son of God, to be one with God, and that faith in him was the only way for us to know God and have eternal life. He appointed 12 apostles to help him with his task who, with 70 others, also travelled around preaching and healing.

• *Jesus — his death and resurrection*

His radical message greatly irritated the religious leaders who eventually arrested him and tried him with false witnesses. The Roman governor unwillingly agreed to have Jesus immediately executed by crucifixion. Jesus' body was placed in a friend's tomb. After 3 days the body disappeared and Jesus appeared in a resurrected form to his disciples over a few weeks before ascending into the sky before their eyes.

• *The early church*

As a sequel to the gospels, the book of Acts describes the events after Jesus had gone, beginning with the arrival of the Holy Spirit to his waiting disciples. The believers continued the work of Jesus — the gospel was preached and many believed, people were healed and demons cast out by the power of God through the ministry of the apostles and others. A community of Christians developed which reflected the principles of love and living which Jesus taught.

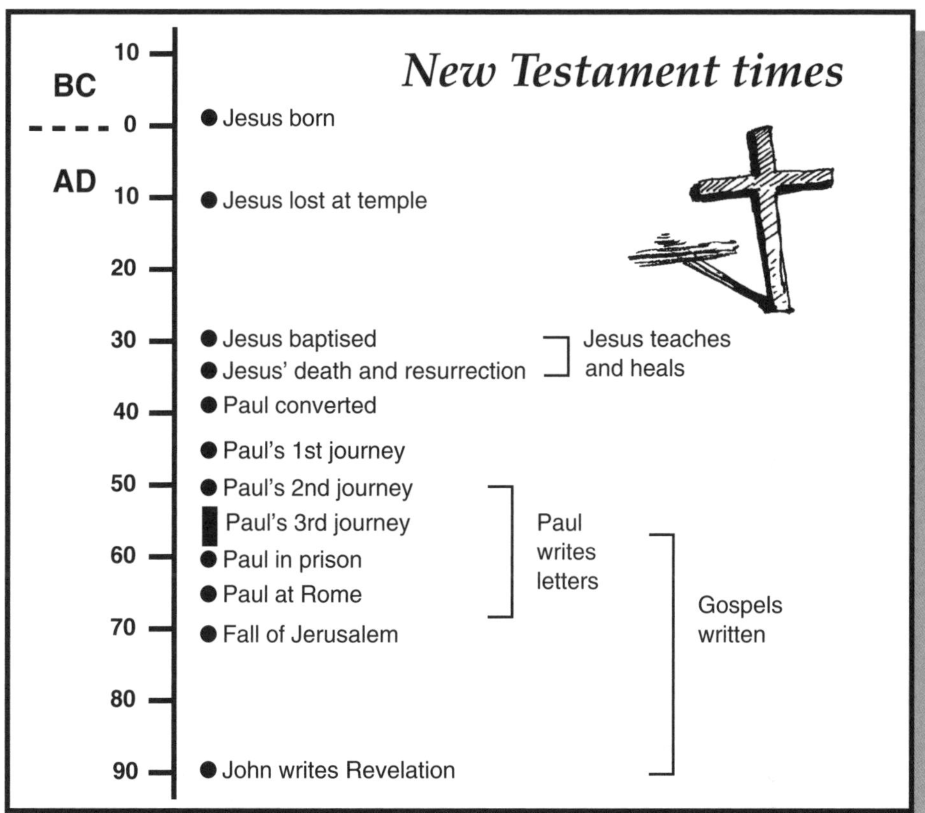

• *Paul*

The second part of the book of Acts relates the exploits of Paul who was an educated Jew from Tarsus who at first was vigorously persecuting Christians. After a dramatic conversion he became a strong defender of the Christian gospel with a particular mission to make the good news known to the Gentiles. He embarked upon a number of dangerous expeditions to preach the gospel from Israel to Greece. His stance offended the Jewish religious leaders and he was arrested in Jerusalem and eventually taken to Rome. There are several of Paul's letters preserved in the Bible — some are written to churches, others to individuals. There are also some letters by James (the brother of Jesus), Peter, John and Jude.

• *Revelation*

The Bible finishes with this prophecy given by John the apostle. It starts with a message of warning and encouragement to seven churches. It then goes on to describe the events leading up to the second coming of Christ and the final judgment. The language is poetic and graphic and portrays the clear victorious establishment of the eternal kingdom of God and the defeat of evil.

How to read the Bible

• *Reading through the Bible*

You can read the Bible like any other book — if you read three chapters a day and five chapters on Sundays, you will get through it in a year! It is a good idea to use a modern easy-to-read version for quick reading and some people keep a bookmark in their Bible and just pick it up and continue reading when they have time. This type of reading will help you to get an overview of the Bible. You may prefer to read the Bible and other books mentioned below online or on your phone or tablet - there are lots of resources!

• *Meditate on a short passage*

There is great benefit in meditating on just a few verses in the Bible and pondering over the meaning of the words. Several organisations produce Bible reading notes which direct you to a short passage each day and provide brief comments to help you get the most out of it.

• *In-depth study*

Detailed Bible study will help you to understand its teaching more fully and will reveal many truths which will help you in your life. This kind of study needs more determination and organisation. You might choose to study a book in the Bible, a word in the Bible, a Bible character, a doctrine or other topic. These studies will take you all over the Bible as you compare one part with another. You should use a translation which follows the original language closely and the books mentioned below will be helpful too.

• *Helpful books*

You will find many helpful books at a Christian bookshop:

A Reference Bible has references in the margin which point to other related texts so that you can tie parts of the Bible together easily.

A Concordance is an alphabetical list of the words used in the Bible showing where they occur. Some Bibles have one included in the back which you can use like an index. An analytical concordance tells you about the original Greek or Hebrew words.

A Bible Dictionary or Encyclopaedia is an alphabetical list of Bible words and topics with explanatory articles giving useful background information.

A Bible Commentary gives valuable background information and thoughts on Bible passages, verses and individual words. It is rather like somebody explaining the Bible to you as you read it. Some commentaries are very long with many volumes.

A Bible Handbook is packed with charts, maps, articles, photographs and it contains a brief commentary on the whole Bible. This is probably the most useful book to help you start to understand the Bible.

A Study Bible is a reference Bible, a concordance, a commentary and a handbook all rolled into one. There are notes and articles on each page near the Bible text.

Original Languages — Much can be gained from reading the Bible in its original languages but not many of us are able to do that! The various types of books above will help you to reap the benefits from those who do know Hebrew and Greek.

Find out what this says!

• *Time and place*

It is good to find time each day to read part of the Bible. Many Christians have a regular quiet time which they devote to prayer and Bible study each day. You will probably find that you can spend more time over the weekend.

Settle yourself down in a quiet place and clear your mind of distractions. Pray asking God to help you understand what you read. The same Holy Spirit who inspired those who wrote the Bible can inspire you to learn from it.

• *Allow God to speak to you*

Expect God to speak to you from his Word. What does it say about:

- God — his character
- The will of God
- Jesus Christ
- Our relationship with God
- The Holy Spirit
- How to live our lives

13No one has ever gone into heaven except
the one who came from heaven–the Son of
Man. 14Just as Moses lifted up the snake in
the desert, so the Son of Man must be lifted
up, 15that everyone who believes in him may
have eternal life.
16"For God so loved the world that he
gave his one and only Son, that whoever
believes in him shall not perish but have
eternal life. 17For God did not send his Son
into the world to condemn the world, but to
save the world through him. 18Whoever
believes in him is not condemned, but
whoever does not believe stands condemned

Also:

- How can you apply the passage to your circumstances?
- Is there any guidance for your life and do you need to act on what you have read?
- You can make notes as you read and underline or highlight verses or words which make an impression on you. You can devise your own colour code for passages of different sorts.
- Try to learn any verses which you have found helpful.

English Bibles

For English-speaking people there are lots of versions of the Bible available. Some are careful translations by a team of scholars, others are free paraphrases by individuals. Some are useful for careful study, others are better for reading to get the gist of the Bible story. They can conveniently be divided into these types:

• *Word-for-Word*

These attempt to translate a word from the original Hebrew or Greek with an equivalent English word. Feature of these translations are:

- They are good for detailed Bible study.
- They can be quite formal and awkward to read.
- You feel nearer to the original language.
- You can use with Strong's concordance which enables you to quickly find which Hebrew or Greek word is being used. You can also use an *interlinear* Bible which has the actual original language under the English text.

Examples:

NASB New American Standard Bible (probably considered to be the most accurate word–for–word translation but a little old–fashioned)

KJV King James Version (traditional English Bible)

NKJV New King James Version(updated KJV)

ESV English Standard Version (a very readable and modern word–for–word translation)

• *Thought-for-Thought*

These attempt to translate the ideas more than the precise words. Some would believe that this is a better way to translate. Features of these translations are:

- They are easy to read and understand.
- Good for personal Bible study and church use.

Examples:

NIV New International Version (a very popular translation in straightforward modern English)

NLT New Living Translation (a modern translation in simple English, very readable)

• *Paraphrase*

These are loose translations for getting the general gist of the Bible. They often use modern idioms. Features of these translations are:

- They are suitable for general reading but not for close Bible study.
- Sometimes give you a new angle on a Bible passage.
- Can be fun to read.
- Sometimes more like a commentary than a translation.
- The translations are often criticised by scholars for being inaccurate.
- Best not to use as your only Bible!

Examples:

TLB The Living Bible (a personal paraphrase of the Bible)

MSG The Message (a very loose personal paraphrase)

What next?

So you enjoyed doing *First Steps*? Why not follow on using *Scenes of Life*? This has a similar format to *First Steps* but is more demanding and covers practical issues of living as a Christian.

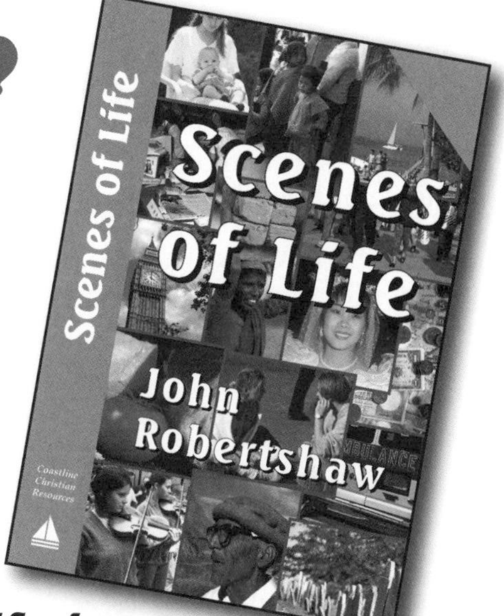

Scenes of Life

20 Bible studies on life issues

Also by John Robertshaw:

Knock Knock !

A brief look at what Christians believe

Baggage Checkout

Bible solutions to life's problems

Bible Plot

Grasping the story line of the Bible

Available from your local Christian bookshop or can be ordered directly from CLC or online.

start at: www.coastline.org.uk

Useful Bible passages

- *God*
  - **The Creator** — Genesis 1, Hebrews 11:3, Job 38:1-39:30
  - **His love** — John 3:16, Lamentations 3:22-24, 1 John 3:1
  - **His power** — Isaiah 40:6-31, Matthew 19:26, Ephesians 3:20
  - **His justice** — Exodus 34:5-7, Zephaniah 3:5, Romans 2:1-16
  - **His care** — Deuteronomy 33:27, Psalm 23, Isaiah 41:10

- *Jesus Christ*
  - **Is God** — John 1:1-14, Colossians 2:9, Revelation 22:13
  - **Eternal** — John 17: 5, Colossians 1:15-20
  - **The Son of God** — Matthew 3:17, Matthew 16:16, Hebrews 1:1-3
  - **His humility** — John 13:1-17, Philippians 2:3-11
  - **A real man** — Hebrews 2:14-18, 1 John 1:1-3

- *Life events*
  - **Before birth** — Psalm 139:13-16, Luke 1:39-45
  - **Birth** — Genesis 3:16, Psalm 127: 3-5
  - **Childhood** — Matthew 18:1-4, Matthew 19:13-15, Ephesians 6:1-3
  - **Marriage** — Genesis 2:18-25, Proverbs 5:18-19, Ephesians 5:22-33
  - **Parenthood** — Deuteronomy 6:7, Proverbs 13:24, 22:6, Ephesians 6:4
  - **Work** — Proverbs 10:4, Proverbs 12:11, Ephesians 6:5-9
  - **Old age** — Isaiah 46:3-4, Proverbs 17:6, Ecclesiastes 12:1-7
  - **Death** — 2 Corinthians 5:1-10, 2 Timothy 1:10, Hebrews 2:14-15
  - **Life after death** — John 14:2, 1 Corinthians 15:12-58

- *Virtues*
  - **Love** — Matthew 22:37-40, 1 Corinthians 13:1-13
  - **Wisdom** — Proverbs 1-9, 1 Corinthians 1:18-2:16, James 3:13-18
  - **Faith** — Matthew 9:29, Romans 10:17, Hebrews 11
  - **Humility** — Micah 6:8, Luke 14:7-11, Romans 12:3
  - **Joy** — Ps 16:11, Is 61:10, Jn 15:11, 16:24, 17:13, Rom 14:17
  - **Patience** — Psalm 37:7, Psalm 40:1, Colossians 3:12-14
  - **Kindness** — Luke 10:25-37, Galatians 5:22-23, Ephesians 4:32
  - **Self control** — Proverbs 16:32, James 3:2, 2 Peter 1:5-9
  - **Peace** — Isaiah 26:3, 48:18, John 14:27, Romans 8:6, Col 3:15

- *Life crises*
  - **Bereavement** Deuteronomy 34:8, Job 1:20-21, John 11:33, 20:11
  - **Divorce** Malachi 2:16, Mark 10:2-12, 1 Corinthians 7:10-16
  - **Persecution** Psalm 59, Daniel 3:16-18, John 15:18-21
  - **Trouble** Psalm 57:1, Psalm 71:19-21, 2 Corinthians 1:3-7
- *Emotions*
  - **Fear** Psalm 91, Isaiah 41:10, Isaiah 43:2
  - **Anxiety** Luke 12:22-34, Philippians 4:6-7, 1 Peter 5:7
  - **Guilt** Psalm 51, 1 John 1:9, Hebrews 9:14
  - **Anger** Genesis 4:6-7, Eccl 7:9, Eph 4:26, James 1:19-20
  - **Sorrow** Psalm 126:5-6, Isaiah 53:3-4, Mark 14:34, Rev 21:4
  - **Depression** Psalm 42, Psalm 77, 1 Kings 19:3-13, 2 Cor 7:6
- *Wealth*
  - **Beware of** Luke 12:16-21, 18:24-25, 1 Timothy 6:6-10
  - **Giving** Matt 6:1-4, Luke 21:1-4, 2 Corinthians 8:1-9:14
  - **Lending** Deut 15:1-11, Psalm 37:25-26, Luke 6:34-35
  - **Borrowing** Psalm 37:21, Proverbs 22:7, Romans 13:8
  - **Integrity** Deuteronomy 25:15, Daniel 6:4, Romans 13:6-7
- *Sinful nature*
  - **Greed** Proverbs 15:27, Ecclesiastes 5:10, Luke 12:15
  - **Pride** Daniel 4, Proverbs 11:2, 16:18, 1 John 2:16
  - **Drunkenness** Prov 23:29-35, Isaiah 5:11, Luke 21:34, 1 Cor 6:10
  - **Gossip** Proverbs 11:13, 16:28, 18:8, 20:19
  - **Slander** Colossians 3:8-9, Titus 3:1-2, James 4:11-12
  - **Jealousy, envy** Psalm 37:1, Proverbs 14:30, 27:4, Galatians 5:19-21
  - **Hate** Leviticus 19:17, Proverbs 15:17, 1 John 2:9, 3:15
  - **Selfishness** Proverbs 18:1, Matthew 25:43, Philippians 2:3
- *Immorality*
  - **General** Ephesians 5:3-7, Colossians 3:5
  - **Sex unmarried** Deuteronomy 22:20-29
  - **Adultery** Exodus 20:14, Proverbs 7, Matthew 5:27-30
  - **Prostitution** Leviticus 19:29, 1 Corinthians 6:12-20
  - **Homosexuality** Leviticus 20:13, Romans 1:26-27, 1 Cor 6:9-11

You could use the following pages to write down more Bible passages which you discover and find helpful.

Notes

Notes

Index of Bible verses

A list of Bible verses used in the 15 units with **page numbers**.

Old Testament

New Testament

Index of topics